A Very Special Team

An Introduction to Team Building in the Dental Practice

by

Bill Whateley

Dental Practitioner
Torquay, Devon

Series Editor
Fiona Stuart-Wilson, MA (Cantab), Assoc. IPD, MIMC CMC

Published by the British Dental Association
64 Wimpole Street, London W1M 8AL

ISBN 0 904 58853 X

Produced for the Publisher by
Chase Production Services, Chadlington, OX7 3LN
Printed and bound in Great Britain
by The Cromwell Press, Trowbridge

To Peggy
Pete and Kate

Contents

Acknowledgements

The central premise of this book is that professional teams are built around professional relationships, and that every relationship affects every other relationship. Thus I acknowledge my debt to everyone I have worked with over the past thirty years, and hope you will accept my appreciation and thanks.

In particular, the current team: Claire McGregor, Louise Reshad, Sue Smythe and Peggy, my wife, who have worked hard and skilfully to build a practice we are all proud of.

And also, Jayne Donovan, who assisted me for thirteen years, sharing our successes, fielding my mistakes, and demonstrating how well a team can work.

The committee and members of the Pankey Association, who continue to demonstrate the enormous value to both patients and practice of working closely with colleagues from all backgrounds in dentistry and from all parts of the UK and overseas.

And finally, my father, who retired early from practice due to ill-health, and taught me to bear suffering with dignity. It is only now, too late, that I can find the words that would have meant so much between father and son. What price hindsight? I hope there is some light within these short pages that will generate a spark for you, the reader, to appreciate the real value of those around you. Time can be short, use it with care.

Introduction

Where the human condition is concerned,
it is better to be vaguely right than precisely wrong,
better to own a fruitful confusion
than to mask it with irrelevant precision.
John Heron

I hope you will accept this book as a place of fruitful confusion! It is an approach to practice, not a prescription for it, a way of looking at it to help you question and clarify your own current situation.

It is about working as a team. Not a football team designed for competition, nor a production team designed to put products in the marketplace, nor even a construction team, although elements of all three are present. It is about a dental practice team, a team designed to provide a sensitive, personal service for those who seek out dental care. It looks at the human side of the practice, the basis for the service that we offer, and without which, clinical, technical and management skills would be superfluous.

The author's starting point is that of a single-handed dentist because that is what he is. But anyone within the dental profession, or outside it, should be equally at home with these concepts. The mark of the professional is not the letters after the name, but the attitude she brings to her occupation—the concept of becoming the very best you can, of being a continuing student in a fast-changing world, of understanding that perfection is a distant goal, and that your current position of 'good enough' is but a starting point for the next step.

The professional builds a career on principles rather than expediency. Yes, there are moments when expediency takes precedence, but the more experienced one becomes the more those moments are the exception rather than the rule. We have to balance the conflicting demands of attaining a high quality in our clinical care with delivering that care to our patients effectively and sympathetically, and, at the same time, backing it up with competent management skills. And we must achieve all this in an increasingly complex, unstable and uncertain world.

This is a book for every member of the team. As we set out to work actively with others, so, inevitably, we develop as individuals. Understanding the process of working together, our part in that process, and the effect it has on us and those around us, will help us provide more effective care for our patients, and contribute greatly to the success of the practice.

Concepts and ideas have been taken from a wide range of sources and are introduced here to encourage you to think about the issues raised, and how they might help you in your practice and your own professional development. Some ideas are presented in isolation to deepen your understanding. But they should always be viewed in the wider context. At the same time, I have tried to avoid too much 'irrelevant precision'. This is an introduction to the subject, an overview for some and a way-in for others who wish to study further. For the latter, a reading list is provided at the end.

I suggest you read it through in a general way, taking note of those paragraphs and sections that seem relevant to you, and then review these areas more carefully at your leisure. Whatever your situation, working with others is a lifetime study.

Bill Whateley
1 November 1998

Definitions

'**A dental practice team**' is made up of a group of individuals able, willing and prepared to work with others while taking responsibility for their contribution to the dental care of individual patients.

I use the word '**patient**' throughout this book because it implies a particular relationship which is not met by alternative, more fashionable words such as 'client' or even 'customer'. Although these last have their place, they only cover a very small aspect of a more complex situation that we shall refer to as '**the practice–patient relationship**'.

I also use '**receptionist**' to cover the more tortuous 'front-desk person', '**assistant**' rather than 'DSA' or 'chairside assistant', and '**hygienist**' rather than 'dental hygienist'.

'The practice manager' and 'the practice administrator' are also involved in the team, but are not directly referred to here.

Rather than add to the confusion of sexes—by using 'he or she' or 'his/her'—where there is no distinction between them, which applies through most of the book, I have used the male or female forms in alternate chapters.

The apparent confusion of titles is a sign of change, an evolution in thinking which, I am sure, will sort itself out in the course of time. Currently, there is even an argument for dropping the distinctions in job titles and referring to each member of the team as a 'dental professional'. I shall not use this term here because it is more appropriate to the text to use the original job titles.

1

What do we mean—'team'?

During the working day, the dentist's world can become focused entirely on the touch of a diamond bur on enamel—the careful weight of the instrument, the sight of it shaping the tooth, the sound changing with the position of his fingers. A small world indeed, but this is a world in which he is master—a world he has studied and trained for.

These sensations of touch, sight and sound are well-known to the musician, and the craftsman, and anyone whose time is spent honing delicate manual skills. But there is one distinct difference. The object of their concentration is inanimate, and the results of their efforts exposed to those who are not directly involved in the creative process. However, the object of the dentist's concentration is very much alive, and always involved in the process that is taking place. And there are others who are working alongside him, supporting his skills and adding skills of their own. Thus the practice of dentistry requires the practitioner to develop not only sophisticated clinical and technical skills, but also skills in developing professional relationships. Without such skills in relating to our fellow men and women, dentistry would remain a technical craft. It is 'people skills' that elevate it to the position of Profession.

A basis of trust

Our success in practice is governed by our patients allowing us to enter their personal world. To earn their permission to do so, we spend time building a level of trust—a trust based on mutual respect. Our success, or lack of it, will colour all our professional relationships. Like surgeons, doctors and others involved in the intimate world of individuals, this sets us aside, endowing a special responsibility to behave honourably and ethically in our dealings with each other.

Working with others: an attitude of mind

If our success is tied up in our relationships with others, it follows that it would be to the benefit of all concerned to create a practice in which such relationships are encouraged to develop and grow. Levin pointed out that the average staff retention (he was studying orthodontic practices) was five years. His study highlighted the fact that a team is a dynamic, finite organisation, having a beginning, a middle and an end. As one person leaves, the old team ends and a new one begins. Another person joins and the relationship-building process begins all over again.

A successful leader will understand this process, and pay special attention to each part of the cycle, balancing the expectations that come with experience against day-to-day reality. If he creates a management structure that allows for flexibility, for example by encouraging team-members to rotate certain jobs, the pool of experience within the practice will develop with a subsequent increase in potential. Flexibility often leads to innovation. Without encouragement, our natural preference for the known can work against innovation, unless innovation itself is made part of the culture of the practice. As the team develops and matures so it creates a momentum which allows it to renew itself when the time comes.

Throughout this book I will think in terms of people. I will take the premise that the practice of dentistry centres around this series of continuously developing relationships, the success of which will have a direct bearing on the success of the practice. The aim is to draw together various concepts and ideas that influence the development of the dental practice team and to place them in a practical perspective. It began as a book about dentists and the teams they work with. However, it has ended up as a book about people. In setting out to describe how to put a team together to deliver better dental care to those who seek it, it ended up describing a practice based on relationships.

At no point does the emphasis on professional relationships deny the need for the highest standards of clinical skills, nor the need to continually develop and hone those very special skills that we have chosen for our careers. It does imply, however, that these skills and knowledge have to be applied, not in some abstract way, but to real live human beings, each one of whom is gifted with a bewildering complexity of physical, intellectual, emotional and spiritual attributes.

And it is directed at you, the reader, whatever your position within the practice. People who are admired for their ability, those who step up to become masters of their profession, consistently possess a positive, constructive, collaborative approach to their work. It is the purpose of this book to help you bring out that collaborative part of you. But it is not a 'cookbook' to be read as a set of instructions. It is designed to widen your vision, so that you can continue the journey yourself (yes, it is a journey). In your personal journey, there is a distinct step to be taken from learning the skills that allow you to work within dentistry to learning how to fit those skills in with the skills of those who work with you.

So, to sum up, I shall look at professional relationships within the practice, how they start on a one-to-one basis and then merge together to form a team. As I do so, I shall shed fresh light on the dentist–patient relationship, and how it might more accurately be called the practice–patient relationship.

2

Your team begins with you . . .

It's Monday morning, 9.30 am. You have had a weekend away from the practice, and here you are, looking around you at the place where you spend more than half your life. What do you see? . . . People? Premises? Rooms? Colleagues? Patients? A group of individuals? A team? A burden? A joy? A source of income? A source of debt? Five days in the way of next weekend's party? A means to help others? A vehicle for your own professional development? An important service in your community? Some of these? All of these? None of these? If you are going to be part of a developing team, then these questions need an answer. It is not who you are in the team, it's the attitudes you bring to it that will govern its success.

Whether you are the principal of your practice, the new assistant or the long-suffering receptionist, your presence colours the team. How you think about other people and working with them matters a great deal to the success of those around you. Be aware that a team is built of individuals. So, whatever the strengths and weaknesses of your colleagues, the first person to take in hand is you! This chapter looks at some of the knowledge, attitudes and skills that lie behind the process known as team-building.

Point one—you do not have to be like everyone else. You have your own talent and experience that you bring to the practice. You are special in your own way and have been chosen to join the team because of that specialness. But, like everyone else, you have to be able to blend your talent and experience with the talent and experience of those around you. This blending, this working together of responsible individuals, and the continual ebb and flow of the relationships that form in such an atmosphere, creates the energy that gives the practice its drive.

First things first

Before we examine this in more detail, there are some questions that need answering. Figure 2.1 invites you to consider your attitude to dentistry. There are no right or wrong answers, each may be right. Alternatively, if your

What is dentistry to you?

- Is it a vehicle for your manual dexterity ... or a service that raises the quality of other people's lives? Or, perhaps, both?

What is your dental practice to you?

- Is it a lifestyle ('this is how I spend my professional life!') ... or a business that you can sell for a profit, or where you earn the salary you need to live on? Or, perhaps, both? (Remember, whatever your position in the team, it's still your practice, regardless of any financial investment or the amount of time you have been there.)

Do you consider yourself to be concerned primarily with illness or with wellness?

- Treating illness .... Creating wellness

Do you think of yourself as dealing with dysfunction or working to improve function?

- Dysfunction ....Function

Do you think of yourself as someone who eases pain, or prevents pain happening?

- Discomfort ....Comfort

Do you think of yourself as someone who restores unsightly teeth, or as someone who uses her skills to enhance a person's appearance?

- Restoring unsightly teeth .... Enhancing overall appearance

Do you wait for people to come to your practice or do you reach out to them?

- Passive marketing ....Active marketing

Do you let the practice manage itself or do you spend time and energy making it work for your patients, your team, yourself and your family?

- Passive management ....Proactive management

Do you think of yourself as the only competent person to make all the decisions in the practice or are you an essential part of the team?

- Stand alone ....Part of the team

Do you think of yourself as a leader, a manager or not involved in that sort of thing?

- Leader ....Manager ....Not involved

Do you think you will be more knowledgeable and skilled in five years time, and that new experiences will develop your attitude to dentistry, or do you think you will be about the same as you are now?

- A developing professional .... A fully developed professional

Fig. 2.1 Your attitude towards dentistry

current attitude is somewhere in between, where would your point of balance be? Regardless of your position in the practice, answer each question in a single, short sentence, and write it down. Later on, when you consider your objectives for the team, your replies will increase your insight.

Take your time to work through the above. Remember, there is no right or wrong answer: the purpose is to help you clarify your approach to your career. Using this information as a baseline, you will gain a greater insight into why you view the practice the way you do. You may also consider that other members of your practice may have a different, and equally relevant, view.

This is our starting point to building a team—if we don't know where we stand on certain basic issues, how can we possibly expect people to work with us effectively? A primary responsibility of anyone involved in the helping and healing professions is to regularly review her knowledge, attitude and skill base. Abraham Maslow, a psychologist who made a very important contribution in the area of personal and professional development, describes 'the good enough professional' '. . . aware of her imperfections, owning them and making decisions about overcoming undesirable traits'.

A personal culture that recognises the importance of others?

It is the dentist who holds the instruments. And, while she is holding them, everything and everyone around her is focused on her skills. She repeats the procedure again and again, becoming ever more confident, and, after a while, that confidence turns into a habit. She really does become the centre of her small world. For the unwary, this world can wrap itself around her. She develops a small mountain of experience, becomes increasingly comfortable with it, and, albeit unintentionally, increasingly isolated from those around her. This world is essentially a world of clinical dentistry, which requires different skills from the ability to deliver a service or to build a business competently. Yet both of these are requirements for a successful practice. If her clinical skills are going to reach the people who need them, she must learn to look outwards, beyond her special expertise. And this requires leadership skills as well as management skills.

Leader versus manager

It would be wrong to describe leadership and management as complete opposites. There are many areas in which they cross. However, there is a difference and it would be helpful to consider the broad statements in Figure 2.2.

- A manager manages; a leader creates the space in which others can manage.
- A manager is appointed (or, in some cases, self-appointed); a leader is created by those who follow her. (A leader is one that followers have defined as being most capable of helping them attain their goals and objectives.)
- Management has tight parameters with boundaries governed by present circumstances; leadership takes a wider view, looking beyond day-to-day influences.
- Management requires rules to work within; leadership requires principles to work with.
- Management is concerned with making the process work today; leadership is concerned with the growth of that process and what will happen in the future.
- A manager needs a leader, just as a leader needs a manager.
- In a dental practice, the management role may be assigned to one individual, but the leadership role may well jump between team-members, depending on the who, what, why, when or where of a particular situation.

Fig. 2.2 The difference between a leader and a manager

How should we behave towards each other?

To make the point clearer, we are going to apply the Golden Rule: 'Behave towards others as you would like them to behave towards you.' The question can then be asked, 'Well, exactly how would you like people to behave towards you?'

Our position in a team is governed by the way we behave towards the other members, their perception of that behaviour and vice versa. Therefore, before we consider the process of team building (chapter 4), we should consider some background factors which, if used appropriately and skilfully, help to make working with others an enjoyable experience. These are:

- positive ways to get the message through;
- an approach to others that encourages them to develop and grow; and
- a framework, in the form of a set of principles to work within.

By itself, each one is not sufficient. Put together they form a firm foundation for working effectively with our colleagues, and creating a caring environment for our patients.

1. Six ways for the message to come through

In this section, I focus on *how* people communicate, rather than when, where or why. By taking an overview of the various forms our communication can take, we can begin to recognise our own preferred, or habitual, style. We can then find the opportunity to widen our communication skills.

John Heron proposed six types of intervention and divided them into two groups: **Authoritative** and **Facilitative**.

Our patients come to our practice because, compared to them, we are an authority on dental care. In our discussions with them about, for example, their home-care regime, we can put our authoritative message over in three different ways.

1. We can be **prescriptive**—we can specify the type of toothbrush, toothpaste, floss etc. and exactly how to use it.
2. We can be **informative**, and spend time explaining the reasons behind it, looking at alternatives, generally educating the patient.
3. We can **confront, or challenge**, the patient by showing her the plaque in her mouth, demonstrating the bleeding and pointing out the consequences of the situation in a more dramatic way.

Fig. 2.3 Authoritative ways of communicating

These, perhaps, match some people's view of the more traditional approach of the dental and medical profession to patients. However, it has always been the case that the more successful practitioners have understood the importance of the facilitative approach—they have the ability to involve their patients in the process of moving from illness to wellness. Moreover, today, the amount of information that is available to patients makes them more educated, confident and willing to take charge of themselves. This demands that those with the knowledge and skills of experience should be able to assess the patient's knowledge and competence, and use this in the process of reaching a successful outcome. This facilitative approach can take three forms (see Figure 2.4).

2. Allowing for growth in the practice

As practitioners, we encourage our patients to develop an understanding of themselves and their dental needs. To achieve this successfully, we

1. It can be **catalytic**, where the patient is encouraged to be more self-directed in solving her home care problems. The intention is to enable her to develop her own approach, perhaps by providing an easy-to-understand monitoring guide, or using a plaque-disclosing agent, or supplying different oral hygiene aids and so on. The dentist still accepts the responsibility for her patient's oral health, but the patient is being encouraged to gradually take more and more responsibility herself.
2. It can be a **supportive** approach, where approval is shown of the patient's intentions. It is a way of acknowledging her and confirming her significance in the process.
3. The third, and, perhaps, least understood, approach is the **cathartic** one. In catharsis, a release of tension takes place, for example with laughter, (but it could equally occur with the storming of anger or tears of sorrow). Laughter is often used to release emotional tension in the practice, because the treatment process itself leads to a build-up of tension. Success depends on the patient and the situation. For example, there is also the occasional situation where a person may be under great tension in her home life. The fact that she is facing yet another problem in her dental condition may lead to tears. By allowing those tears to flow, the team shows empathy towards the patient and the problem is eased. This is not to imply that members of the dental team should consider themselves expert enough to actively indulge in personal therapy, but that they are aware of their significance in the lives of their patients.

Fig. 2.4 Facilitative ways of communication

ourselves need a deeper understanding of the process of personal and professional development—the process of change. If we have no experience of it ourselves, how can we possibly understand it in others? Indeed, the whole concept of 'wellness' involves a widening experience of the world around us, and a subsequent change in our perception of it. The practitioner sets out to create a space for the individual to grow into, a choice of directions. In the case of a patient, this might involve different treatment plans for the same problem. The practitioner must look beyond the immediate influences of the current situation to 'what might be' for this person. In short, she needs to be sensitive to her colleague's ongoing needs. This means continually listening to them.

Carl Rogers, another important psychologist in the personal and professional development field, devoted a lifetime's study to the conditions that were required for a person to develop to her full potential. He put forward three characteristics of a relationship that can create the most fertile conditions for growth. These are empathy, non-possessive warmth (a non-judgmental acceptance of the person), and congruence (see Figure 2.5).

Empathy is the 'ability to stand in the other person's shoes', to see the situation from her point of view, and to be able to communicate that understanding. It differs from showing sympathy, which is viewing another person's situation through your own feelings about that situation. In this case, your emotions may or may not be the same as those of the other person. In a situation where a person needs space to reflect on her feelings, imposing yet another set of feelings merely adds to the problem.

Although showing sympathy is a perfectly valid way of relating to another person, in a professional relationship where a certain amount of growth, development, or healing is required, the practitioner who can develop empathy, and not allow her feelings to impose, will be rewarded with greater success. The skill comes in balancing the two.

A warm, positive, non-judgmental acceptance of the other person also encourages growth. This means not just accepting that part of a person that we like and rejecting every other characteristic. It is learning to accept that person for the total being they are. At this level of understanding, unacceptable behaviour or miscomprehension can be worked on in a positive manner. There is more mileage in accepting a person for who they are, and helping them overcome a particular difficulty, than in rejecting that person because of the difficulty itself. The perpetually grumpy patient, or the man from the fish shop who fills the waiting area with the smell of fish, or the lady with the badly behaved children, all create certain challenges to our appreciation of them. Very often the challenge is on the surface only, and once acknowledged it resolves.

And finally, to experience **congruence** in another is to 'somehow trust them because we sense that they are being who they are, that we are dealing with the person herself, not with a polite or professional front'. Most of us will have no difficulty recognising incongruence in someone on television, for example a politician 'towing the party line', or a stage actor in a television commercial. It causes unease, but not because of the message itself. Our thoughts tune in to the discrepancy between the person and what he or she is saying, and, as a result, failing to get across. The more genuine and warm the person, the more genuine the acceptance by another, and the better the conditions for the relationship.

Fig. 2.5 Characteristics of a relationship for growth

These are background skills to help you develop your practice team, and are a valuable resource in your search for a leadership style. As attitudes in our dealings with others, they provide an invaluable frame of reference.

However, if we are going to achieve a balanced approach to building our team, and not just an unconnected group of skills and attitudes, there are other avenues that need to be explored. In particular, we need to take another step in our personal journey, and try to understand why it is valid to use these communication skills in the first place.

3. A principle-based practice?

In his book, *The 7 Habits of Highly Effective People*, Stephen Covey puts forward a strong argument for using principles in the pursuit of a successful personal and business life (see Figure 2.6).

I hope it is evident that these principles are *congruent* with a professional approach to the practise of dentistry. They provide a solid base upon which to build our teams, and also to underscore our practice–patient relationships.

Putting it all together

However, there is another step in this process: it's not what we know, it's what we do with what we know that makes the difference. If a set of principles is important then an understanding of how those principles are put over is equally important. I talked above about developing first a vision for the practice and then a disciplined approach to achieving it. Your vision comes from your deeper beliefs, your world view (sometimes called your paradigm), and the lifestyle you wish to create from that. Only you can answer for you. For some people, this comes instantly, for others it may take time and, whichever the case, your vision will be a developing one that may change with age and experience.

If you are going to develop a positive, growing relationship with those around you, they need to understand what is expected of them and have a definite structure they can fit into. This structure is made up of a series of systems (or routines), which are the basic units on which the practice is run—not just clinical systems, but service and management systems also. For example, it is as relevant to have an established system for writing a welcome letter as it is to have a system for root canal treatment. The way these systems fit together is reflected in the format of your practice manual (see below).

Ultimately, team members and patients are 'buying' the sum total of your systems, even if they are only conscious of one aspect of them. The rest, albeit out of sight, also have an effect. Therefore, getting to understand

- They are **proactive**. They take the initiative and responsibility for making things happen.
- They **begin with the end in mind**. They don't step into a project without a clear vision of the end result. They monitor their progress continually, and are not afraid to alter their plans if appropriate. For example, a two-year plan for the practice may need to be altered if new technology, new equipment or new techniques demand a fresh approach to its management.
- They **put first things first**. This could be the title of this book. If we don't do the preparatory work in planning our practices, how can we monitor where we are going?

  Using these three principles enables the person to break the potential habit of relying on others, which can hold back her ability to act for herself.
- They **think win/win**. They treat life as a co-operative, collaborative venture. Whatever the undertaking, unless both parties stand to gain, in the long term both sides lose. A continuing preference for one member of the team may boost that person in the short term, but it will be at the expense of the goodwill of her colleagues, and a loss of the spirit of the team.
- They **seek first to understand, then be understood**. They take the trouble to see the other person's point of view, before their own. This doesn't negate their own viewpoint, but puts it in context, so that an educated decision can be made. This directly reflects Carl Roger's 'empathy' described above.
- They **synergise**. They believe in teamwork, that the effectiveness of two or more people working together is far greater than them working independently. This is the basis of the Master-Mind Principle, described in Chapter 5.

  These three help them interact effectively with other people, and are the three characteristics that, above all, mark your colleagues as team players. And, finally,
- They **sharpen the saw**. They are continually practising the previous six principles. They cultivate the process of continually developing their skills.

Fig. 2.6 Suggestions about successful people (Stephen Covey, 1989)

your systems, how they link together and the effect this can have on the members of your team is part of your preparatory work.

This means that attention to detail in establishing and putting those systems together will also govern the success of your new practice. The more that is left to chance, the more that chance will take a hand, with uncertain results. Further, if people are to be made to feel important, your practice structure—people, organisation, management, systems and marketing—needs to be put together in a way that builds relationships, not drains them . . . and quickly, because you have only a year or two to establish a successful pattern. Take too long, then the practice may easily slip into habits that make it difficult to emerge into the next phase of a development programme.

Monitoring development

In a world of change, how do you know how far you have come if you have no record of where you have been or where you want to go? If you are serious in your desire to develop yourself, your team and your practice, then you need a way of recording progress—a diary, or notebook, that you can adapt and re-adapt to match your changing needs and aspirations in your rapidly changing world.

This is a management tool, that can be adapted to suit the person using it. What starts as a reference source, containing a valuable address list and a developing index of relevant information, can progress to a daily organiser and on to a practice manual/journal format. By providing a copy for the whole team, a practice resource is created where information can be passed between team-members in a manner that is in keeping (congruent) with the style of the practice.

Traditional methods of publishing have meant that diaries, however well produced, became dated very rapidly. But now personal computers have created a wide variety of publishing options, and, with them, the opportunity to be increasingly innovative. You are putting together an asset that will be useful in five, ten or twenty years' time, increasingly reflecting your progress, whether it be, in purely professional terms, your knowledge, skills and attitudes or, in a wider context, your intellectual, emotional, physical and spiritual growth.

Thus, when choosing a diary system, the remit should be for a publication along the lines of Figure 2.7.

A loose-leafed format encourages and allows for adaptation as a diary/planner, journal, handbook or manual. A page size of A5 is large enough to be useful, in that this paper size can be handled by even the

- Can be used as a diary—on a daily, weekly, monthly and yearly basis.
- Can provide an address list which can be used for contacts and referrals, as well as personal data.
- Can be a notice-board, and record, for courses, relevant events, publications etc.
- Can allow the inclusion of one's own notes/thoughts/inspirations etc.
- Is capable of adding further pages from a wide variety of outside sources.
- Is flexible enough to allow for regular, and irregular, updates, to cope with changing, and as yet unknown, needs well into the next century.

Fig. 2.7 A diary system

simplest of computers. On the other hand, it is not so large as to take up too much space.

The recommendation for a printed system rather than an electronic one is not to deny the usefulness of the latter. Electronic systems, like the palmtop organisers, are very useful—indeed, I use one alongside a printed diary system. The point is that it is the *discipline* required to produce the printed version, and the ease with which information is accessible, and can be shared with the team, that makes it an effective resource for a dental practice. There is a power in the written word that is not available to words that languish in the memory of a computer.

Summary

In this chapter I have suggested a personal approach to creating a practice in which a team can flourish. This includes:

- questions to help you clarify the attitudes that lie behind your decisions;
- different approaches when communicating;
- attitudes and skills that allow people to grow;
- a set of principles that provide a growth-oriented background;
- a means of gathering relevant information together and monitoring its relevance, both in current terms and in terms of your progress towards the vision that you have set for yourself.

Now we have established this, I can move on to the next stage—developing a one-to-one relationship with each member of your prospective team.

3

it builds on one-to-one relationships . . .

Before we look at how we might put together a team, it would be helpful to look at the formation of the professional relationship that underlies that team, how it works at various levels and the vital significance of one aspect of it—trust.

Mrs Jones' story

'Good morning. This is the dental practice. Sally speaking. How can I help?'

'Oh, hello, this is Mrs Smith. I haven't been to your practice before, but I would like to make an appointment to see the dentist please. My friend Mrs Jones has highly recommended you.'

Mrs Jones. We remember the first time she contacted the practice three years ago. Such a timid, nervous voice on the other end of the phone—'. . . scared of dentists', '. . . teeth out as a child', '. . . in pain, gums bleeding', '. . . can I come tomorrow?' And we gave her an appointment and she came the next day. And she was afraid, very afraid. She sat in the waiting area—comfortable chair, relaxing decor—shaking. She'd got this far, 'no way' was she going further. And Sally, the receptionist, sat with her, talked with her and listened to her, and then quite suddenly Mrs Jones got up and said, 'I'm sorry, I've got to go.' And she went.

Next day, she rang again, 'I'm very sorry about yesterday. I'd like to try again.' So we tried again. This time Jill, my assistant, spoke to her, 'Hello, Mrs Jones, it's good to meet you. How are you feeling today?' Tense voice, tense body, clenched hands. Words said, 'Very well, thanks.' Body said, 'Awful!!!' And I came and said hello to her, and we found a quiet seat away from everyone, and gently we began to find out what the problem was.

It was like starting to cross a bridge, a very high and very long bridge, with words like fear and anger and anxiety and unknown dentist and strange staff and bad experiences written all over it. Yes, she had a painful tooth, but it was nothing compared to the emotional pain she was carrying. We started very slowly and tried one step at a time.

We eventually got her into the chair, and, very, very gently, we stopped the pain—but she remained extremely anxious. A week or so later, she did come back, and she allowed me to find out more about her—her previous experience, her anxieties, her physical health—and to examine her carefully—the neglected mouth, one or two broken-down teeth, discoloured composites, bleeding gums.

What she needed was obvious to the whole team, but not to her. She still couldn't see past her anxiety. So I said, 'Mrs Jones, I understand you are afraid to let me do anything for you, but your gums do bleed very easily and you say they are sore. We have a lady here who can help make them healthy. Would you like to see her?' And she said she wasn't sure, could she meet her first. So we asked Rachel, our hygienist, to come in. And they talked for a while, and the outcome was an appointment to discuss her dental home care.

Now, something happened during that appointment. Whatever it was, it encouraged Mrs Jones to make further appointments and, as well as improving the health of her gums, we were able to remove the decay and put her on a holding programme. She returned to see Rachel at regular intervals, and her home care skills improved. However, even after a year of coming to the practice, although she was obviously a lot more comfortable, she was still nervous about facing anything other than simple preventive and maintenance visits, and she needed much more than that if she was to avoid losing her teeth later.

And then, out of the blue, we made a breakthrough. A chance remark about one of our relations, and out it came—all her worries and concerns about her daughter. We had assumed that her habitual air of anxiety was still to do with dentistry, which was why we had decided to delay the restorative work still further. But we were wrong, the problem was no longer with us, it was elsewhere.

Once we understood that, all our attitudes changed. Mrs Jones became much friendlier and more open, and the team responded accordingly. We had shared a special part of our lives, not a particularly happy one as it happened, but certainly a private area that none of us had been privy to before. And it turned out that, yes, she was ready for the restorative work that we had been putting off, and we were able to enter that phase of her treatment. A few months later, we had reached a new and much more stable level—one of optimum health, comfort, function and appearance, a situation that had seemed impossible two years before. Mrs Jones had finally crossed the bridge.

And now, three years after that first tentative phone call, 'Yes, Mrs Smith, we'd be delighted to see you. Mrs Jones is a very good friend of ours too.'

Towards a professional relationship

What had happened in those three years? Is there a lesson in this extreme, but in no sense unusual, story, that we can apply to other situations, in particular the building of our team? To find an answer, it is helpful to divide the transformation from terrified onlooker to enthusiastic friend into a series of steps.

That first phone call took us from the point of no contact with Mrs Jones, no knowledge of her in any way, to that first **acquaintance**, that first moment when you become aware that this person exists and is significant in some way. This is a step we experience frequently in our daily lives. In most instances, these contacts are random and unplanned (the shop assistant, the ticket seller and so on). They may or may not lead further, but if they do lead further, it is our first impressions of each other that can be very significant. This is especially true in the case of a new patient.

Mutual respect
Mutual acceptance
Rapport
Acquaintance

Fig. 3.1 Stepping towards a professional relationship

First impressions

This is the moment you share with every patient who has ever sought your services. It may come on the telephone, or when the doorbell rings, or in reception or even the surgery (although preferably not the latter). It is that defining moment when you meet each other for the first time. At no point in your whole relationship will there be a more significant moment. Some may be more dramatic, or more interesting, but these are underlined by that first meeting. And it is just as important for you as it is for your patient.

Does this mean you have to be especially formal, or friendly, or 'nice'? No, it means you have to be aware that this is the first time you have met this person and that the impressions that are made at this meeting are lasting ones. You are meeting for the first time someone who may wish to trust their dental care to you—for a few months, or a few years, or maybe the rest of their life. It is, therefore, imperative that the impression you make is sustainable, and not one 'made up' for the occasion. This is Carl Rogers' 'congruence'. To build a relationship on false impressions, whether it be a professional or a personal one, is to risk alienating the other person, or, at the very least, committing yourself to be someone you are not. It has been said that when a person is pleased with your services they will tell one or two of their friends; when they are displeased they will tell twenty acquaintances. That first contact is as much a practice-builder as any amount of sophisticated marketing.

This applies to your team also. Just as the first contact with a new patient is important, so is your first contact with each member of your team. This may be that first advertisement in the newspaper, or that first mention of your practice by a friend or an existing patient, or the first telephone call to the practice. Every team-member should be aware of this. It may be obvious to say it, but an advantage for a potential team-member must be their ability to make good first impressions. Who is the best at this in your team? Will the first meeting be with that team-member or with you, the dentist? Where is that lasting impression coming from?

It does matter how you project your practice and your fellow team-members to the outside world. However, you may never know what people's first impressions are; very few will tell you, and often only if it is favourable. Whatever the impression, be delighted to get honest feedback. In the next chapter we look at this in more detail, but, at this stage, I am concerned only that you recognise this as a vital step in a delicate process.

Rapport

In the case of Mrs Jones, who so obviously was afraid to see us, but equally obviously decided she had to make the effort, there was one of two ways in which the relationship could have gone. Her first impressions could have been negative (and, for her, they didn't have to be very negative, she was halfway there already), and she would have had no more to do with us. Alternatively, they could have been positive enough for her to want to know more.

What actually happened was that the first telephone contact was positive—she came to the practice—but the first personal contact, despite the very warm attitude of our receptionist, was only lukewarm for her and she left. However, it was positive enough for her to decide to come back for another try. (Yes, she was in pain, but she had been thus for several weeks. She wanted to find a sympathetic practice first, then get pain relief second.)

The 'positive' element she was looking for, but would not have been able to describe because of her anxiety, was exactly what Sally had been trying to create for her—good 'vibes', otherwise known as **rapport**. In that first contact on the telephone, Sally could only make educated guesses at what might constitute rapport with Mrs Jones. In the event, a genuine understanding of what it is like to be afraid of the dentist allowed her to say enough of the right things to give Mrs Jones a hint that it would be safe to at least visit the practice. Because of Mrs Jones' extremely negative attitude to dentists, moving from that first contact to establishing a little rapport involved Sally in taking a risk—she offered sympathy which could easily have been misconstrued and have resulted in a good patient being lost to the practice.

I have used Mrs Jones' story because it has elements in it that highlight the steps in a relationship. These are steps that apply to all relationships, and may or may not be so sharply defined.

All positive relationships show a degree of rapport. The greater the rapport, the more open, more learning, more creative the state between you. It contains a certain comfort that leads the relationship onwards—'I am Mrs Jones, you are Sally, you may be able to help me.' If we slip out of rapport, we start to defend ourselves against the other—'I am me, and you are you. We are separate.' Or 'I am Mrs Jones, you are the dentist.' End of story!

Working in a team, we also look for rapport with our fellow team-members. It may differ from member to member and from time to time, varying with the natural ebb and flow of a normal relationship, but it is a major ingredient in the glue that holds the team together.

From rapport to acceptance

However, it wasn't until Mrs Jones had been to see the hygienist that she began to relax a little, to worry less about what might happen to her and more about how to prevent it ever happening again. Rachel's obvious rapport with her began to melt the barriers, and little by little she became more interested, and then involved. So the real breakthrough came after a number of contacts with the practice. All that had gone before, over the phone or with the other members of the practice, was the prologue to this.

There is a temptation to believe that if we, being highly trained and experienced in the art and science of dentistry and used to seeing a wide variety of people on a daily basis, make our practices attractive places to be, everyone who comes to see us will automatically feel comfortable and safe with us, and accept our care, skill and judgement. This is not so.

Comfort and safety comes once we reach a certain stage in a developing relationship—there appears a feeling of mutual acceptance between us. Yes, our training, our experience and the attraction of our premises may, and often will, contribute to that acceptance, but they are not the primary factors. What is sought is a much wider communication between us, a development of rapport that says, 'Yes, from what I have seen and heard and sensed so far, this practice is the right place for me to be', and the reciprocal, 'From what we have seen and heard and sensed so far, we would like this person to be a patient here.' In Mrs Jones' case, it took a relatively long time to reach that stage of acceptance. In a mature practice, with patients referring their friends and acquaintances, it will often take a much shorter time—but, always, this stage must be reached.

Therefore, if this is the level on which most professional relationships are conducted, then relationships between team-members should be at least at this level. Otherwise, how are they going to recognise the cues that change the interaction from one of 'finding out about the practice' to one of 'being ready to accept the care, skill and judgement offered by the practice'. This level of acceptance within the team includes a willingness to disclose one's professional competence, a strong factor of which is an ability to listen to others. (Note how concepts from the previous chapter are coming out in this chapter.)

Listening

Perhaps the single most positive skill required in the development of a professional relationship is the ability to listen. It is an activity every bit as skilful as the most delicate of clinical procedures. You are listening non-judgmentally, not only to the words that are spoken, and the meaning that is intended, but also to any other meaning that may be implied. And you are listening to the pauses, and the silences; and listening with your eyes—to the way a person sits and communicates physically with you. And you are learning to avoid interrupting and altering the flow until you are sure that all that was intended to be said has been said.

From acceptance to respect

However, once we have learnt to listen to the person—to understand him more ('seek first to understand'), it is possible for the relationship to reach a deeper level and still retain its professional quality. This is what happened with Mrs Jones. It followed the conversation about our respective relations—in her case, her daughter. The subject had not come up before, and, although we knew Mrs Jones had a daughter, we had no idea that there were family difficulties. The outcome that I am highlighting here is not about the specific content of the conversation. It is about the increase in self-disclosure, that led to a deeper mutual understanding, which, in turn, led to a greater respect for each other (the channel for that respect being our separate approaches to problems that affected us both). Bud Ham suggests that 'when people meet in face-to-face interaction, they will come to respect one another if they meet in a state of equality'.

The outcome of that interaction was a considerable increase in the factor that defines a professional relationship—trust.

Building trust

Trust is the *result* of the relationship, not the object of it. The object is to build the relationship in the first place. Nobody said, 'Trust me' to Mrs Jones, nor was it underlined with a loud clap of thunder, it just happened in the course of time as the relationship developed. I cannot be certain that our conversation was pivotal in Mrs Jones' decision to accept her restorative treatment. I do know, however, that she made it shortly afterwards, and in a positive manner that implied confidence in her decision, in the outcome of that decision and in our part in it.

Of course, it could have gone the other way. By not listening to her, or putting undue pressure on her, we could have reduced her trust at any time. In fact, there was a moment during treatment when she did experience some discomfort. Because it brought back some of her past experiences, she had to make a decision as to how to handle it. In the event, she was able to shrug it off—because of all the positive work that had gone on before.

The experience of trust between two people, or even two organisations, has been likened to maintaining an **emotional bank account** between them. Positive experiences count as a credit into the account. Negative experiences count as debits. The greater the credit in the account, the more it is able to bear the debits. This concept of a relationship emphasises the dynamic aspect of it. The more proactive both parties are at building the relationship in a positive way, the easier it is to bear any negative periods. In the normal ebb and flow of life, negative periods do happen. If the positive side of the relationship has been neglected, it will inevitably cause greater friction than might otherwise be the case.

Does this apply to building a team?

Of course it does. We are talking about relationships—ongoing, developing, professional relationships. How would Mrs Jones have fared in a practice whose team-members had no clue to the relationship they were building? What are the chances of them having that clue if they haven't experienced it themselves? OK, so we can do some things by the book, but how much more effective is the team that experiences the growth of mutual respect between its members.

How do you create that experience? By finding ways of making the positive aspects of teamwork meaningful for the individual team-member. Train, acknowledge, reward, celebrate! Even if there is a serious purpose behind it, it still can be fun! Enjoy it! Those who enjoy working together, enjoy working with their patients, and their patients will respond accordingly. And they will also move through the process that leads to oral stability in health, comfort, function and appearance. And they will tell their friends—and you will do the same for them.

Summary

In this chapter, I have looked at aspects of building a professional relationship, including;

- first impressions;
- rapport;
- listening;
- mutual respect;
- building trust;
- making this a valuable part of the team-building experience.

In the next chapter, I move on to forming the team itself.

4

it develops into a small group of dedicated professionals . . .

Planning the team

A beginning, a middle and an end

However much you like the members of your team, the chances of you being together for life are slim. It is not a marriage contract! Your team's time-span might be measured in hours, days, weeks, months or, preferably, in the case of a dental practice, years. But be aware, it will have an end.

For a group of self-aware team-members, the knowledge that this is a finite organisation can give them a special bond. 'We are only together for a while, and all we have is each other. Let's make the most of it.' This marks the point at which the team settles down. In the lifecycle of a team, it is known as the 'norming' stage.

The lifecycle of a team

A team is a vital, dynamic group of people. This vitality can be recognised as stages in a lifecycle (see Figure 4.1). There are four of them.

- **Forming**—with each new member and/or fresh activity, the team starts by getting the measure of each other for the job-in-hand.
- **Storming**—as time progresses, team members' individual personalities and approaches to work start to assert themselves. There can be clashes of personality at this stage and a certain amount of disorganisation.
- **Norming**—'We are only together for a while . . .' The 'rules of the game' are set.
- **Performing**—the team settles into a comfortable way of working, and can now start to make decisions more quickly, and get results.

Fig. 4.1 Stages in the lifecycle of a team

If the team has a single purpose, then the cycle repeats itself. However, in a complex situation like a dental practice, teams will switch between stages each time they encounter new issues to resolve.

This 'storming' stage is the critical time. The longer a group remains intact, the more familiar its members are with each other, then the less time this stage lasts. However, if too many new issues are introduced at once, the team gets marooned in 'storming' mode and less is achieved, (although a mature team can use this as a highly creative period). It is up to the leader to keep an eye on what is going on, get a feel for the stage it is in and what it can bear at any one moment.

Do we need a team? Can't we manage without one?

If you are the dentist, it isn't you who arranges the date and time for each appointment, is it? It happens at reception. Someone else takes responsibility for your patient, as well as your schedule and your assistant's workload. After the appointment is over, someone else will make sure you, or whoever is responsible, will contact your patient and check that the after-effects of the procedure are minimal.

And while all this is going on, there are other patients to care for, either directly—those who have come to see the hygienist, or the other dentists in the practice—or indirectly—telephone calls to be taken, appointments arranged, schedules printed out, billing, receipts, letters and so on. In short, while the dentist is immersed in his clinical world, a much larger and equally—yes, equally—important world exists around him. Other people are as concerned with your patients as you are.

Perhaps, the dentist and one assistant can juggle with both the administrative and the clinical side of the practice for a short period, but taking on an extra one, two or more people to look after the rest of the practice will surely allow the dentist and her assistant to focus on the patient in the chair. The result is an improved service.

Creating your team

If it requires a certain skill to build professional relationships on a one-to-one basis, it requires an equal, and slightly different, skill to put two, three or more such relationships together to create a team.

Firstly, you must recognise that you don't create the team, the team creates itself. Your task is to create the conditions in which the team can form. It is not a question of you selling your ideas to a group of people to make them into a team, rather of them buying those ideas from you and weaving a team from them.

Start with a design

We are going to consider your ideal team for your dental practice. Your team will be different from the next one. The idea that yours will be the same as the team in the practice down the road is complete nonsense. Personalities differ. So, just as you cannot restore a person's mouth without a full examination and a well constructed treatment plan, so you cannot build a team without a similarly well constructed plan that takes into account your particular situation. By building a logical plan at the outset, even if you have to adapt it in the light of circumstances, you are working from a sound position. Building a team 'by the seat of your pants' is tempting fate.

For the purpose of this book, we are going to build a very simple team to run a single-handed dental practice (single-handed in the sense of one dentist). Although the situation may be more complex in larger practices, the basic elements that apply here are the same. You start by reviewing your previous experience, then, having assessed your current situation, you move on to evaluate your practice needs.

Beware of labels

At this stage, you should be(a)ware. We are going to apply a series of labels to people. Some of these labels are obvious—age, sex, occupation—but some are more subjective on our part. The people we actually employ in our team will most probably not slot neatly into our theoretical niches. There is a danger in a practice applying such labels in response to the currently accepted theory of the person making the judgement. They are then constantly reinforced. However, as we work more closely with people, get to know them better, and watch them develop in their roles, so such labels become less and less relevant. People are people—labels are labels. They are useful to provide a 'way-in' for the inexperienced to widen their skills in the art of relating to others, but they should be kept strictly for planning purposes only.

Criteria for team-members

What sort of people do you want to work with and have help you build your practice? You are the one putting the team together, and, as I have said earlier, the starting point is yourself. Everyone has to relate in some way to you. Even if you are not responsible for putting the team together, you are part of it, it is still your team and the exercise is important to you for exactly the same relationship reasons.

Professional relationships do not necessarily have to be close, but they do have to be effective within the dental practice setting. Therefore, your reaction to your fellow team-members is as important as their reaction to you. For example, how do you feel about people in the following categories?

- **Skills:** Clinical, technical, clerical, computer? High manual dexterity, practical, not good with hands?
- **Age:** Young, middle aged, older?
- **Sex:** Male, female?
- **Previous experience:** Experienced, less experienced, no experience? Experience with children, adults, the elderly? Surgical experience, preventive counselling, marketing, computer, accounting? No clinical experience, no administrative experience?
- **Personal Style:** Assertive or less assertive, emotional or less emotional (amiable, driver, expressive, analytical—see social styles in Chapter 6)?

What positions must they occupy?

- Dentist, chairside assistant, front-desk person, hygienist? A combination—all of the time, some of the time?

When are they going to be in the practice?

- Full time or part time?

What are the wider roles that need to be filled to make the team run effectively?

- We will need '**outside people**'—those who can represent our practice to the outside world, and
- '**inside people**', those who beaver away within the practice and make it work.
  (Remember, in a small practice, people fill several roles.)

We are looking for individuals who can develop the practice . . .

- a **Thinker**, someone who mulls things over, and retains an overview of what is going on;
- a **Researcher**, who listens to patients—records their likes, their dislikes and their history; who goes through the catalogues, looks at the journals, rings the library, watches the videos, goes on the courses . . . (This is the sort of person who breaks deadlocks in the practice and moves things forward);
- and a **Co-ordinator**, who clarifies what is needed and sets the agenda.

We need people who can rise to the occasion . . .

- a **Problem-solver**, who enjoys the challenge of working things out . . . (how are we going to keep that appointment schedule manageable?);

(continued overleaf)

- a **Shaper**, who moulds the solution and innovations into the overall plan;
- and a **Specialist**. No matter how talented or intuitive we are, we often need professional skills we cannot hope to master ourselves in the time we have available. It may be that we can take someone into the team who has these skills, but increasingly we will have to buy these, and accept the expense. In the 1990s, specialists, inside and outside dentistry, have become much more sophisticated about the value of their abilities and how to charge for them. It follows that there is an advantage in developing as many skills as practical within the practice.

At the same time, we need people who know how to work well . . .

- a **Team-worker**, who promotes unity and harmony, and counter-balances friction and discord. (Of course friction happens. Remember, the ebb and flow of relationships? She carries people through the 'storming' periods.) In a practice environment, every member must accept this role to a greater or lesser extent;
- an **Implementer**, who translates theory into practice and gets the job underway. This role is especially important in maintaining the momentum during courses of treatment, making sure that the right appointments for particular patients are scheduled properly and followed through;
- and, finally, a **Completer**, the compulsive meeter of deadlines and fulfiller of schedules. This is the person who clears up the loose ends and leaves us free to carry on with the next project . . .

Fig. 4.2 Ideal team roles (with acknowledgement to Belbin for the wider roles)

All the above roles are valuable. By not paying attention to a particular one, the team becomes unbalanced and less effective. Obviously our team will begin with people who are naturally disposed to one or more of these roles, but who must, over time, learn to appreciate and handle most of them. So, if we apply the concept of 'wellness' and acknowledge there are choices in the way we can develop, we have now created a 'virtual' team into which your new people are going to grow. We have not hampered them by assigning fixed positions. There is a freedom that working in such a team will bring out.

Part of your planning process will be to identify the roles that are appropriate to each practice routine (see Chapter 1). Having done so, you can judge the balance of roles you need, and build a clear idea of the sort of person you are looking for. In a quality practice, where systems are reviewed continuously, maintaining this team balance, which naturally ebbs and flows with the development of its members, is essential.

More questions

If you were putting a team together for your practice, exactly how would you balance the above roles? Do you think they are relevant? The willingness of a patient to come to your practice might be based on a particular person she meets when she gets there just as much as on the clinical service offered. The person favoured may be the dentist but may equally be another member of the team, or it may be the team atmosphere as a whole. Do you know enough about your patients individually to understand whom they may prefer and why? Over a long period, this may affect the type of person who comes to you, and, if that team-member leaves, that will affect the practice. You may be pleased about this or you may wish to change it. If you wish to change it, where will you start?

The practical needs of a dental practice

To get a more realistic idea of what our team might look like, we must decide what we are asking it to do in practical terms. There are three overlapping activities in a dental practice that a team needs to serve. These are **clinical** activities, **service** activities and **management** activities. The details of these activities are outside the remit of this book, but it is possible to break them down into categories.

Clinical activities:

- Caring for patients
- Two- four- or six-handed dentistry
- Operatory preparation and maintenance
- The developing and mounting of x-rays
- Stock control
- The continued development of clinical and technical skills

Service activities:

- The delivery of dental care appropriate to the patients' needs
- Education in home care
- Reception duties
- Answering and using the telephone
- The development and maintenance of a practice image
- Quality review
- The continued development of service skills

Management activities:

- Storing, retrieving and maintaining patient files and records (both manual and computer-based)
- Answering and writing letters
- Running the recall system
- Maintaining a fee system that is understood by the patients and gives an appropriate return to the practice
- Dealing with the sale of home care items
- Problem-solving and goal-setting
- The continued development of management skills

Fig. 4.3 Different team activities in a dental practice

They are all important for the balanced running of the practice, and your team will need to cover all of them. This is the 'virtual' practice into which your 'virtual' team will grow!

Write it down

You should now transfer your overview of your team *to paper*. Do not underestimate the power of writing things down. There is an added dimension to your decision-making that no amount of deep thinking, or burying information in a computer, will achieve. Use your computer for sifting information, and, once you have refined your wording, print it out and place it in your diary where you can review it regularly.

Statements of aims and objectives

The next step is to put the aims and objectives that apply to your team into the form of statements—separating your overall aims from your current objectives. (Your objectives are the steps you are taking this year to achieve your long-term aims in the future.) Try to use two A4 sheets, one side only, no more. This is a helpful exercise whether you have been practising in the same practice with the same people for many years or whether you have just started. This is a statement you are going to review regularly—certainly annually, but in a young practice more often.

Aims

Write down your aims in two sections. Head the first one '**. . . as they relate to our patients**', and the second one '**. . . as they relate to us**'. Each section will be a distillation of your beliefs in those areas. For example: the first two paragraphs of my practice statement as they relate to my patients are:

> *We are building a dental practice for those people who value our service for the quality it adds to their lives.*
>
> *More specifically, we are setting out to help our patients retain their teeth for a lifetime in optimum health, comfort, function and appearance . . .*

And the first paragraph of the second section '. . . as they relate to us' reads:

> *We have been trained in the advanced clinical skills necessary to assist at the chairside, and also in the wider skills needed to provide the comprehensive service designed to achieve the above. The experience of starting a new practice will develop those skills even more and will be of enormous benefit outside the practice and in later life. Because we live in a world in which the leading edge of technology changes almost daily, we are inevitably in a process of continuous learning, and this will be boosted through courses, seminars, in-house study and so on . . .*

These are extracts from longer statements, which were written when planning a new practice.

Objectives

The **objectives** statement has a series of bulleted objectives under the following headings:

- Clinical and technical dentistry
- Service
- Fees
- Staffing (teamwork)
- Timing.

My 'objectives' statement crept on to a second page—I reduced it from four pages and, in the end, decided that I had refined it to be 'good enough'! This particular statement covered the first two years of the new practice, and was reviewed regularly. Reading it now, almost two years later, provides a very valuable insight into how much has been achieved in that time.

The practice blueprint (1)

You now have a series of four written documents stating your aims, objectives and personnel requirements, in terms of the roles that they need to occupy and the activities they are expected to carry out. These are statements, not a set of rules. They are guidelines, based on your current perception of your future needs. They can be added to or refined further in the light of circumstances. Ideally, they should come from you, written in your own words. However, if you haven't the words yourself, then use those of a practitioner you respect, someone whose ideas most closely match your own. After you have reviewed them once or twice, they become yours, and your practical experience will allow you to refine them appropriately.

Armed with these, you are now ready to get started, because these documents are not just for you, they are for your whole team. They form the background to all your transactions with your fellow team-members. They are an essential part of your **practice blueprint**, and will be presented to each person in whatever form you choose: perhaps in diary form, an A4 file or folder, with or without other information about the practice.

This 'blueprint' is the precursor of your practice manual, and is designed to give the team a start. Once time has passed, and everyone has practical experience of how the practice actually works, then the manual (see later in this chapter) can be created from a 'hands-on' perspective.

Putting the team together

How will you find your team?

By this stage, you should be confident that you know the sort of person you are looking for. Now comes the point when you look for the real people!

The advertisement

So, logically, you look in the places that the type of person you are seeking is most likely to be seeking you. It might be the local newspaper, it might be a dental journal, or a trade journal, your local sixth form, or by word-of-mouth via friends or colleagues. Remember that your advertisement will represent your practice to more than the current job-seeker. Others will read it too. If it looks interesting/exciting/fulfilling in some way, they may tell a friend or consider applying for the position themselves at a later date.

Build a list of applicants. These days, job-seekers are encouraged to apply to businesses for jobs whether the job exists or not. The sort of people who have the get-up-and-go to contact you first are the sort of people who take responsibility for themselves and will not hold back when it comes to communicating with your patients—a positive point in their favour.

What else will you need?

. . . a written application with a CV. This is your first screening. But written applications and CVs don't necessarily tell you all about the person, so, having eliminated the more obvious non-contenders, get a senior member of the team to ring them up, speak to them first and then put them through to you. This is your second screening—an informal chat about the job and what the applicant is doing currently. You and your team-member, who will be as interested as you and probably able to glean more, will each form an opinion. From your discussion, a short-list of three is invited to an interview. Bear in mind that people who talk well on the telephone are not necessarily good in a face-to-face situation.

The interview

The object of an interview is to find out as much about the candidate as possible. Therefore, ask the right question, then shut up and listen!

Create a series of questions, ten or a dozen will do, that are relevant to your practice situation. Somebody else's questions won't do, because the answers will have no real meaning for you. This is not an exam, this is the first step in what may prove to be a professional relationship lasting five, ten, fifteen or more years. Yes, for most of the candidates it may be the only time you ever meet, but are you prepared to lose a real winner? The time to tell the candidate about the practice will come later—at this stage it is you who needs to have the answers and be able to compare this candidate with that candidate. Therefore, put the same questions to each, and score the replies in some way (e.g. a 1–10 scale).

Your questions should seek out areas that are relevant to your practice. For example, why do they want this position? How would they fit in with your team? Are they intuitive, or must everything be spelt out to them (both can be relevant)? How do they feel about themselves? Are they sensitive to other people? How caring are they? Spend time drafting your questions. You are trying to find out those aspects of the candidate not covered by the hard facts contained in their CV. And as you define your questions, define your ideal answers. Will the successful candidate need to answer every question as you do, or differently? And if so, how differently? Which is more suited to the vacant position?

Once you have interviewed them, find a way for the team to interview them as well. This is not just your team, it is the whole team's team! If the person you have chosen is suitable only to you, then you may be in for a long stormy period from which your team may or may not settle down. That is not to say you should accept collusion from the others to employ the 'easy' candidate, merely that you should recognise the challenge. You then have a choice. If you choose to take on the candidate, then the negotiating exercise will have strengthened their position; if you choose not to take them on, then the negotiation itself will have deepened your and your team's understanding of what you require in a new recruit. To avoid the issue altogether is to weaken the team.

Raising performance

Now that your team has a new member, how will you reach your anticipated standard of practice?

This is a team that cares for others—it will be more effective in doing so if it cares for itself, and its members care for each other. For example, take the case of the appointment running well over time and patients being kept waiting. If they are nervous, or new to the practice, or have been kept waiting before, the way your team handles the delay can make or break the moment for them. It's not just the job of the receptionist to be aware of this—yes, she's in the front line, but who's looking after her and keeping her informed of what is going on? Remember, it's your team, it's your assistant's team, it's your hygienist's team, it's your receptionist's team—it's our team!

At the same time, there is a wider view. The central purpose for your practice is not the forming of the team. The central purpose is the creation of the conditions necessary to improve the quality of life of those who seek your services. The point is, you can't do it alone. You need people to help you. And, as we have already mentioned, to become a team, these people must buy the conditions you have created.

In the 1990s, these conditions focus on more than clinical needs. They have to do with the way those clinical skills are presented and delivered, i.e. service skills, and the business skills that back it all up. Your team has to buy all these too, or it will be a very short-lived team, or worse, a group of uninvolved individuals—no team at all.

But what exactly does each member of the team see when they look at the practice? Because each person is unique, they are all going to see it from a slightly different viewpoint. This can be helpful because it broadens your approach, but it can also create a problem, unless you make it very clear what you are looking at, (e.g. you see the fulfilment of your vision, but the others may see long hours of work away from their families; you see a chance to work together, but they see you going off at an apparent tangent on courses and disrupting the routine yet again).

So we need to clarify what we are trying to achieve.

Employment legislation—the baseline

We have been looking at team-building in terms of creating an environment in which the formation of a caring team is inevitable. Indeed, if we achieve this then we are well on the way to creating an environment in which it is possible to practise truly excellent dentistry.

At a different level, employment legislation is designed to create a working environment in which the rights of both the employee and the employer are protected. It is useful to note that, in a democratic society, legislation is a rolling process, continually being challenged, reviewed, modified and improved upon. Its value is built up with experience. The value of your team and practice will grow in the same way.

In the United Kingdom, employment legislation is based on giving people justice and equity, job satisfaction and democracy. The implications of such legislation must be noted and complied with for two reasons: firstly, because it is the law of the land, and secondly, because it gives shape to certain aspects of your team environment. We have been discussing an approach to reaching the highest standards in working together. At the other end of the scale, legislation gives us a marker which our standards must not fall below. In effect, it provides a foundation to build on.

Contracts of employment

The list of employment rights for the individual is comprehensive. It includes: salary, hours of work, holidays, sickness or injury absence and pay, pensions, how much notice can be given, grievance, the rules of the practice, disciplinary procedure, changes in terms and conditions of employment and maternity arrangements and pay. (For a fuller understanding of the details see the British Dental Association's Advice Sheets D1—Contracts of Employment and D2—Conditions of Employment for Dental Nurses. There are further Advice Sheets in this series, which deal with the employer/employee relationship.)

A paradox

At this stage, we have a choice. On the one hand, we can look at employment legislation as a hindrance to our team-building—'surely, it takes us away from the real focus of the team, if we are working so well together, we don't need it!' On the other hand, we can take a wider view—'well, although we are working well together, people's circumstances can change without warning, (e.g. illness, injury, personal problems at home and so on). A mature, sophisticated team understands this and respects its member's need for formal security should these situations arise.' As with all contracts, one hopes never to need them, but the responsible employer and employee both know that the unforeseen can happen. The wise team reviews contracts regularly, perhaps annually, to take note of any changes in circumstances.

An opportunity

If we continue to take the wider view—that employment legislation is a valuable factor in a professional working relationship—then, instead of setting it aside for a rainy day, we can use it in a positive way to strengthen that relationship. This legislation falls within the practical aspects of team-building. Thus Terms and Conditions of Service can be written to include your own standards as well as the legal standards required.

So the next question is, 'With legislation as the bottom line statement for our developing team, what are the steps we need to take to work the team up from this level to the standards that we have envisaged?'

Building the team approach

We are now working on the assumption that the new team-member has been in the practice for six weeks, and the experience has been a positive one for all concerned. If it has not been so, then, at the end of the three-month trial period, she will leave. This will often involve a certain sense of failure on both sides, but this can be mitigated by a positive approach to references and help and advice in finding a more suitable position. It is not wrong to employ the wrong person or accept employment in what proves to be the wrong position. Mistakes happen. It is how one copes with the situation that is the sign of a mature team approach. A dental practice is a special environment, we need to be sure this is what we want before making a long-term commitment. We often need to experience it to make up our minds.

The practice blueprint (2)

The practice blueprint is made up of a series of statements about the practice and is presented to a new team-member within the first three months. If the practice is a new one, then the whole team will be presented with a copy at the same time (as previously mentioned), regardless of how long they have worked together. Its purpose is to ensure that the whole team has a written framework within which they can work. It reflects the overall *attitudes* that prevail within the practice—'this is what we think here'. At the same time, it defines the position of the individual team-member within the practice. It differs from a practice manual (see later in this chapter) in that the latter is concerned with detailing specific systems, clinical, service or management systems—'this is how we do it here'. In effect, the blueprint is designed to help team-members understand their role. It is a form of recognition and acceptance—'you are now part of the team'.

Your blueprint might contain:

- a personal letter, welcoming the team-member to the practice, discussing her role in the team and explaining what is contained in the blueprint;
- the original statement of Aims and Obligations of the practice (see p. 32);
- a statement of Expectations (see below);
- the overview of chairside and administrative activities in the practice (see p. 31).

Other contents might include:

- a patient flow chart;
- the practice philosophy on prevention;
- whatever is appropriate for this particular team-member, in this particular practice, at this particular time.

Remember, this is 'what we think here'. Its main purpose is as a statement of attitudes. It is an opportunity to re-establish the original reason for the person joining the practice and to establish new objectives. Depending on the person, we might choose to include the Terms and Conditions of Employment in this document, or we might feel it more appropriate to do so at a separate meeting.

The 'Expectations' statement

If the Terms and Conditions of Employment provide the bottom line for our working together, then we need an indication of the topline—what is expected of us. In the beginning, for the newcomer to the team regardless of their previous experience elsewhere, these can be set out in a simple 'Expectations' statement written by or on behalf of the practice owner, (in this case, the dentist). Statements will vary from practice to practice, but an example, taken from a new practice, is illustrated in Figure 4.4.

Two points should be made about this statement. Firstly, this is a sensitive area. It is a statement of trust, and, as such, is a step forward in a developing professional relationship. Don't make it if you don't feel able to keep it, especially if it is not in line (congruent) with your beliefs. The damage will be far worse than if you had not made it at all.

Secondly, even though it is a difficult area, loyalty, confidentiality and support are high on the list of our patients' expectations. If we cannot manage it between ourselves within the practice, how can we possibly guarantee it to our patients?

You can expect from me . . .
apart from my statutory obligations as an employer

Loyalty

- This practice is being built on the simple idea that '*the practice*' means the people who run it and the patients who receive the benefit of it. (The premises, equipment, systems etc. are the vehicles we use to provide a professional service.) Therefore, I have a responsibility to you to see that you are kept informed of what is happening, and especially of changes that will affect you.
- I also have a responsibility to represent you outside the practice, particularly as we continue to develop closer relationships with other practices around the country and overseas.

Confidentiality

- I appreciate that there are many more things going on in your life than are immediately concerned with the practice. And, because there are only a few of us, this inevitably means we have a closer relationship than might occur where there are many more staff present. We will certainly learn more about each other than might otherwise be the case, and therefore I undertake to maintain your confidence at all times.

(continued)

Support

- If you are going to help maintain the high standards that we are promising, you will need to be continually learning, both in the practice and on seminars and courses. I will undertake to help you learn within the practice, to arrange more formal learning for you outside it when you are ready, and to support you in whatever way you need. I want these to be enjoyable experiences.

I expect from you . . .

apart from your statutory obligations as an employee

Loyalty

- This is your practice and you represent it—to existing patients and to potential patients, within the dental profession and outside it. I look to you to promote it to your best ability.
- I also expect you to make known those areas that you think can be improved upon—working *with* us to build it to its fullest potential.

Confidentiality

- Apart from your professional obligation to maintain the patients' confidentiality at all times, I trust you to maintain the confidence of all of us within the practice.

Support

- I shall continue to study, to innovate, to try things out and occasionally to make mistakes. There will be times when I am successful and there will be other times when I am less than successful. I look for your support in both situations, and expect the same to apply with every other member of the practice.
- Finally, if the time does come for us to part, I have invested a great deal of time and energy into creating a practice in which you are a very valuable member. Replacing you will be difficult and will certainly alter the balance for those of us remaining. Therefore, if possible, I would like as much notice as possible and your goodwill in finding a replacement, and will likewise help you in whatever your future might hold.

Fig. 4.4 A sample 'Expectations' statement

The maturing team

A team that is performing well must, by definition, consist of a group of people who are learning to accept and work with each other's strengths and weaknesses. Following closely behind 'accomplishing the task', the sign of a successful team will be the development of its members' strengths and a reduction in their weaknesses. In a dental practice, where the emphasis is on the provision of dental care, there are two factors that, by making them a central pillar of team management, develop attitudes in the team-members which actually enhance their service to their patients. These two factors are support and motivation.

Support

Support can be divided into four areas and remembered using the acronym FACE. The areas are:

- **F**eedback
- **A**cknowledgement
- **C**oaching
- **E**ncouragement.

Feedback

Feedback is a powerful motivator. It is an indication that the job we are doing is important and it also fulfils an expectation that comes from our childhood—what we do deserves some sort of reward or, occasionally, punishment.

However, good feedback is difficult to achieve without a positive working relationship between the parties involved. It can easily be mistaken for criticism, which brings out the defensiveness in us (the punishment side of expectations). What we are looking for is how our action appears to the other person. We may or may not require some help in moving on by reinforcing that action or correcting it. It will depend on the other person's role. For example, feedback from a team-member about the way we managed a certain routine situation with a patient will warrant a discussion on how we might do the same thing in the future. Feedback from someone training us in new skills may require more direction in how we should improve. (To get a clearer understanding of this, it might be helpful to review the 'six ways for the message to come through' in Chapter 2.)

The most helpful way to give feedback is to concentrate on the person's actions, rather than on the person herself. The effect should be 'I am enjoying working with you, but in this particular situation, this is the result of what you did . . . ' Highlight the relevant action. What was the impact of this action? And, if appropriate, what are some acceptable alternative outcomes? The outcome of the feedback itself should be to leave the person free to develop appropriately, rather to feel a need to justify the action taken.

Feedback should be given in a consistent manner. Swinging from overkill to pussyfooting leads to a mild form of shock, followed by anger which is defensive, and the intervention has failed. Feedback has been described as 'telling the truth lovingly', and the best feedback should be experienced as a gift.

Acknowledgement

As individuals, we have few greater wishes than to be recognised for ourselves. This applies as much in the work place as outside it. If we are to accept responsibility in the practice, then we accept it as a member of a team, which means that our position within that team needs to be acknowledged. Moreover, it would help to have some acknowledgement that our actions are acceptable, even appreciated by those around us. This is not a sop to our vanity, but a need to know we are heading in the right direction.

If we know we are appreciated, then we will feel better and ultimately do the job better. At the same time, things don't always go according to plan, and sometimes there are very strong challenges that we have difficulty in overcoming. Knowing that others recognise this also is a great help. Empathy as much as sympathy would be appreciated here (see Chapter 2).

Working with others day after day, it is very easy to develop a routine that acknowledges the person's presence, but not their achievements. Routine is, by definition, the usual, and our usual working practice is on a level that after a while fails to stand out. We forget that we are making significant achievements of great value to our patients on a daily basis. So we must create situations where those achievements are recognised.

On a simple level, Frederick Herzberg noted that 'praise is a powerful motivator'. It needs to be given in a certain way:

1. describe the action you want to praise;
2. give the praise;
3. give the reason for the praise;
4. do not qualify it with 'but . . . '.

Practice meetings are an ideal place to acknowledge achievement—in front of the whole team. This formal meeting is the place in which the practice is shaped. What have been informal discussions between individual members of the team can now be given air, and opinion sounded out. Does that mean team-members will always agree or accept these ideas? No, of course it doesn't, but you will have created a starting point, and as you work together more closely and recognise your mutual approaches to tasks, challenges and problems, so you become a more closely-knit unit. A decision has to be made, but, before that decision is made, you will have involved every member of the team, given them a chance to be involved in shaping what, after all, is their team too.

Part of that shaping is to recognise their importance in it. Therefore, we create goals for individual members of the team, acknowledge their achievement and place praise where it is due (but not otherwise). As a team, we can also build shared goals, for example financial ones or ones involving an increase in the service we offer. These must be acknowledged and praise given when due. So the practice meeting becomes a place where goals are set, information provided, success acknowledged and current systems reviewed. By scheduling them through the year, the emphasis can be modified and used to develop the practice positively.

As far as acknowledgement is concerned, sharing a social event, perhaps a meal together, or a visit to an exhibition, is also valuable. It is part of recognising each other as individuals with lives of our own that have aspects that don't necessarily revolve around the practice.

Coaching

The aim of coaching is to be able to delegate, to get those jobs done which, although you are often capable of doing them yourself, frees you and the rest of the team to provide a higher standard of care for your patients.

The best coaching comes in small doses. The object is to assess the coachee's current knowledge, attitudes and skill and their willingness to undertake the task and then to build on this. A general assessment will have taken place at the initial interview, but the details are going to be filled in 'on-the-job'. An initial three-month trial in the position will give the new team-member, as well as the rest of the team, a chance to assess her suitability for the job.

In his book, *The Tao of Coaching*, Max Landsberg suggests four different approaches the coach can make to the coachee, depending on this initial assessment. The coach, who could be any member of the team, not necessarily the dentist, can use delegation, excitement, guidance or direction to team-members as a whole or individually as shown in Figure 4.5.

1. Delegation

Where team members are skilled and enthusiastic, which was probably high on the list of reasons they joined the team in the first place, then the coach can move straight to delegating the task, giving them freedom to do the job, encouraging them to take responsibility and stretching them when appropriate—but always being aware of progress.

2. Excitement

On the other hand, not all tasks engender enthusiasm, and a degree of motivation and encouragement may be required. (Skills may be high, but the will for the job may be low.) Foch said, 'there is nothing so powerful as the human soul on fire'. Well, we can't always 'set their souls on fire', but we can light the match!

As mentioned above, one of the results of a successful team lies in the reduction of individual weakness. These weakness may lie as much in the person's attitude as in their skills. A mature team built on an open trusting relationship, with a healthy reservoir of goodwill on all sides, will ease through the problem quicker than one that is still in its infancy. It takes time to build enthusiasm, and the coach will want to monitor progress carefully and provide regular feedback.

3. Guidance

For a procedure or system in the practice to be effective, new skills are going to be required. With an enthusiastic team, there is no difficulty as far as encouragement is concerned, but training will be necessary. The earlier this starts the better—a new technique learnt on a course, or a new piece of equipment or state-of-the-art material will soon lose appeal and momentum if left 'until later'. By making innovation part of team development, in a risk-free environment that allows for early learning and early 'mistakes', progress will be rapid. In this case, the coach's task will be to explain, train and answer questions, and then gradually relax control of the process as skills increase.

4. Direction

Even in the most successful teams (in fact perhaps this is one of the reasons that make them successful), there are occasions when people are asked to undertake tasks that they have no previous training for, and, quite frankly, cannot see why they should be involved at all! Perhaps a team-member from the front desk is asked to spend time as a chairside assistant, or vice versa, or a visiting dentist or other team-member has been asked to join the practice for a while. Maybe, in the ebb and flow of daily life, there are personal difficulties outside the practice that have distracted one or two team-members. Here the coach has a more difficult task. She must have a clear plan of what is to be achieved and take charge—allowing team-members to fall into place once they have assessed the situation.

The coach needs to provide a clear explanation of what is involved including a vision of the result, and to identify the benefits to the practice and to individual team-members, i.e., she starts by working on attitudes (motivation) then onto skills, structuring the training for 'quick successes', with frequent feedback and praise. The object is to nurture the team by providing clear supervision, rules and deadlines. As progress is made, so she can gradually relax control.

Fig. 4.5 Four different coaching approaches (Landsberg, 1996)

Coaching sessions

In a practice where innovation is built into the culture, coaching is an on-going process. Landsberg suggests a four-step structure to a coaching session, using the acronym—GROW:

- **G**oals
- **R**eality
- **O**ptions
- **W**rap-up

Goals are made for the task-in-hand taking into account the longer-term development objectives of the team and its individual members. **Reality** is an assessment of what has been effective and what has not been so effective. **Options** provide a list of alternative directions and **Wrap-up** concludes with a firm objective and a deadline for its completion. The session might take, for example, twenty minutes at monthly intervals. It might be part of the regular practice meeting, or become a separate session.

In the time between meetings, five minutes now and then providing feedback, and a minute or two praising results (unqualified praise—the word 'but . . .' is not used), would work towards a more friendly, open, trusting environment. The value of involving everyone cannot be understated. Coaching is about correction rather than criticism. It is easy for one member of a team to feel out of favour with the rest of the team if the coaching onus is placed on her shoulders while the rest of the team appear to be 'getting away with it'.

At the same time, in a team that provides a non-confrontational atmosphere, it should be possible for any member to see a need, either for the team or for herself, and to seek coaching. Taking control of one's own future means being aware of weakness and closing the gaps. And this is where encouragement, in the form of motivation, comes in.

Motivation and encouragement

There is a delicate, and crucial, line to be drawn between motivating people and manipulating people. Ultimately, we cannot motivate anyone, people motivate themselves—the longest-lived teams are those to which members choose to belong. However, what we can do is to create the conditions in which motivation, and, in this case, team development, is not only possible, but inevitable.

Needs

Abraham Maslow argued that people are motivated by their needs in life, and that these needs occur on a distinct hierarchy of levels. In a simple form, these can be broken down into three levels:

- low-level needs—food, clothing, housing;
- middle-level needs—a secure job, reasonable working conditions, reasonable pay;
- higher-level needs—the need to belong, to be in control, self-fulfilment, pride etc.

In the environment of a dental practice, with an established and developing team, most people are motivated by higher-level needs. These are the need to be part of a group, the need to be in control, the need for personal pride and the need for self-development and self-fulfilment. From this, we can work out what will be motivating and demotivating in the practice.

Demotivating situations

Examples of demotivating situations might involve a reduction in middle-level needs, for example, if the team-member were asked to take a cut in salary, or if the employment conditions were reduced to part time, or if extra tasks were assigned that were outside the original job description and were unsupported by recognition and/or special training.

Or higher-level needs might be reduced—where there had originally been a promise of job advancement, this was ignored or not forthcoming. Further examples might come from the dentist herself—a refusal to delegate, being inconsistent, being unwilling (or unable) to praise, having a lack of clear direction, not keeping the team informed, being aggressive and/or bad-tempered.

Motivating situations

Hertzburg pointed out in the 1950s that, despite popular perception, salary increase alone was not enough to motivate employees. This is because once a need has been satisfied, it ceases to be a motivating force. Thus, if the middle-level need of a secure job and reasonable pay is met, attempts to improve them will have little effect on motivation as far as the job is concerned. On the other hand, as we have noted, reducing pay will demotivate because the basic need is no longer being met.

The level of salary for a particular practice is generally based on a percentage of gross takings (e.g. 20 per cent). Bud Ham suggests that individual salary is taken as 'compensation commensurate with contribution'. He also suggests that, as with patients' fees, it is a balance between what the patient (or practice) is happy to pay, and the dentist (or employee) is willing to accept.

Although these may at first seem rather vague statements, they emphasise the fact that there are two parties involved in the transaction (Stephen Covey's 'Think win/win'—see Chapter 2). If they are working as members of the same team, then compensation, including salary, will be based on *mutual* respect. As a team, we are asking our patients to pay a fee for our services. We set that fee with consideration of the financial value of the task—the cost involved in providing it and the profit required. It is, or should be, a balanced transaction, just as the salary provided by the practice to members of the team, including the dentist, should also be a balanced transaction.

In some spheres of dentistry, the word profit has gained a negative meaning. I understand that the word profit does not have to have the unspoken words 'excessive ... ' nor 'manipulative ...' placed in front of it, but it is the target of any business that wishes to remain vital. It is of no benefit to our patients to run a practice at a loss. The service will inevitably reduce and it may result in the closure of the practice altogether. If this were to happen, in the long term, we would have done our patients a great disservice.

Therefore, once we have dealt with the middle-level needs, then the jobs that motivate will be to do with meeting higher-level needs—increasing the variety of skills in the team (perhaps rotating jobs), or making each task significant and creating an identity for the team-member involved (recognition, taking care to maintain a flexibility within the job structure), trusting the team-member and giving her the freedom and responsibility to undertake specific tasks, and giving positive feedback and praise. Trust is very important in motivation. It has strong links with responsibility. Trusting someone enough to give them responsibility is motivating in itself.

How does the rest of your team know what your standards are?

You've got to tell them, continuously and consistently—yes, verbally at meetings, but also in writing, in the form of written systems and procedures for the practice—**a practice manual**. The manual is both a guidebook and a rule book on 'how we do it here'. Where there is a need for rules, as in the prevention of cross infection, health and safety legislation and so on, then the manual contains rules. Where guidelines are more appropriate, for example in the handling of patient fees or follow-up appointments which depend on the individual patient, then guidelines are more appropriate.

Your practice manual is an evolving reference work for each member of the team, and, as such, it makes sense to give individual team-members, as they become more experienced within the practice, the opportunity to produce sections of it, and, perhaps, use this as a basis for a practice meeting. This brings an element of research (it need not necessarily be time-consuming or arduous), and presentation skills into team-development.

Quality review

If the entries in the manual are dated, then, as it develops over the months and years, so it is possible to review progress over that time, and to assess the quality of the practice. Just as the clearer your goal, the better your chance of reaching it, so the better the monitoring of your progress, the better able you are to make educated decisions on how far you have come, how far you have to go and what the next step should be.

In a fast-changing world, no practice is a complete, finished organisation. It is a classic example of work-in-progress. Your practice manual is an evolving record of the systems and procedures of that work-in-progress, just as your accounts, whether recorded on computer software or manually, are an evolving record of the financial aspect of it.

A transition—the loss of a team-member

At the start of this chapter, I said that the team has a beginning, a middle and an end. Inevitably, the time will come when a valued member will leave. It should never be a surprise but often is, not because a properly managed team that has built up a clear structure in which to work cannot absorb the change, but because of the sense of loss that occurs. It's rather like an amputee feeling the missing limb long after it has gone. A team is a living organisation. It has a self-esteem that comes with its success in meeting its challenges. Losing a member creates a sense of uncertainty. We miss the person who has gone and recognise that it will never be the same again. We need to adjust. The old team is no longer. We must start again, building on the strengths and weaknesses of the new member and blending them with the strengths and weaknesses of those that remain.

The longer people have worked together and the more closely-knit the practice, the longer and more complex the transition period. It is a time to acknowledge the loss, but also to accept that this is a part of life, a moving on, no better or worse than in countless other daily situations. Except perhaps, that in a team based on caring for the individual, there is a lesson to be learnt—a deepening understanding of those around us and a consequent lift in the value of that care.

5

it reaches well beyond your practice walls . . .

Within the profession, there are four groups of people who come under the heading of team-members, even though they do not necessarily work within the practice—technicians, members of the dental trade, specialists and colleagues.

Technicians

Like dentists, technicians live in a world that demands expertise, service and management skills. The technical skills required are expanding and, with the advent of new materials and a whole new field, implantology, the demands are becoming greater and specialisation common. Although their service is designed for the patient, its immediate focus is on the dentist and his team. Therefore, the team-building skills discussed in previous chapters apply, but in this case there is an extra hurdle to overcome.

A developing relationship

Unless the laboratory is on the premises, actual face-to-face meetings are less common. Moreover, as times change, we cannot automatically assume that an established routine will work between us just because it always has in the past. Where case requirements are more difficult, it is easy for misunderstandings to arise. In a successful practice–laboratory relationship, both parties work not just to anticipate potential problems, but also to design ways of making the relationship more effective, i.e. they are actively looking to develop the relationship.

Two levels of communication

In such a team-oriented atmosphere, communication between practice and laboratory takes place at two levels. The first is at the level of dental practice to dental laboratory—two equal businesses, requiring mutual information, mutual prescription and mutual support. The second is at the level of the job-in-hand, also requiring prescription, information and support (feedback, acknowledgement, coaching where appropriate and encouragement). The balance is governed by such qualities as the length of time the practice and laboratory have worked together, and the technical difficulty of the job-in-hand.

Traditionally, the practice–laboratory relationship grew on the basis of a prescription from dentist to technician on what was required—end of story. Both parties made educated assumptions about the other's approach to the case, and accepted the sometimes variable quality that resulted. It is to the credit of the professional skills of both dentist and technician that they worked together so productively.

The quality practices and laboratories of earlier days maintained a working relationship based on the methods of communication open to them then—telephone, car, feet, post. In the 1990s, electronic communication has opened up wider possibilities, bringing the dental laboratory closer to the practice in terms of information-sharing. E-mail and digital imaging expand the potential for improved quality. The technician can now become more involved in the step-by-step treatment process. For example, the greatly enhanced aesthetics of modern porcelain demand a disciplined approach that make communication between patient, dentist and technician crucial.

A two-way flow of information

Moreover, it is in our patients' interests that we continually monitor the evolving pattern of new techniques, materials and equipment. This requires a steady flow of information between practice and laboratory—a two-way flow of information. It is easy for one party to hold on to information in the mistaken belief that the other possesses it in equal quantity. For knowledge to become skill, first everyone needs to know the details, then they must create ways amongst themselves of converting those details into reality.

A system of communication

Many of the following are already in use, and none need be time-consuming once set up (see Figure 5.1). However, they should be as much part of the preparation for team-building as the activities mentioned in Chapter 4.

1. A written acknowledgement of the expectations of the dental practice regarding the dental laboratory and the laboratory regarding the practice.
   - No two laboratories or practices are the same. Therefore, the least they can do for each other is to discuss their expectations and come to an arrangement as to where their parameters lie—what they will accept and not accept.
   - Is this an easy arrangement to make?—for some it is, for others it is very difficult.
   - Should it be written down, or can we just talk about it?—a written document can be reviewed and updated, and the review doesn't need the presence of both parties.
   - Is it open to misunderstanding?—perhaps, but more than one's memory of a conversation? Probably not.
   - Surely, you are talking about a contract?—not in the legal sense. It is an agreement between professional people who have a mutual respect for each other.
   - How did they get that mutual respect?—they worked at it! (See Chapter 2.)
2. Laboratory prescription slips with space for feedback on the standard of the work done as seen by the dentist,
   - in terms of the above agreed standard;
   - bearing in mind the requirements for effective feedback.
3. Practice feedback slips on the standard of the work done by the dentist,
   - as seen by the technician in terms of the above agreed standard.
4. The discussion on shades and technical details in the surgery with the technician and patient and other team members present.
5. A visit by the practice team to the laboratory, reciprocated by the laboratory team.
6. Shared courses—seek out those courses that are relevant for both dentists and technicians.
7. An occasional meal together, or a social event.
8. A monthly meeting.
9. An annual general meeting!

Fig. 5.1 A system of communication for a dental practice and technician

But I am a crusty old dentist and he is a smart young technician; how will that work? The same way as with a smart young dentist and a crusty old technician (or even a crusty young dentist and a smart old technician)—you can work it out and do what is appropriate to make the relationship effective. If you cannot work it out, then review your commitment to each other. The object is to be proactive, and, if it doesn't work the first time, try it again, or do it another way. Success is in doing, and learning from it, and doing again in the light of that experience. The greatest obstacle is the fear of trying in the first place. And if you do get it right, does that mean you are members of the same team and will work more effectively because of that? Absolutely!

Members of the dental trade

The dental trade is the supporting industry to the dental profession. The major players in the industry are worth many, many times the average dental practice in financial terms. The investment in equipment, stock, personnel and training in a fast-changing industry is increasingly large. The need to keep the books balanced and have continued growth within the organisation is ever-pressing. And yet these firms rely for their survival on a profession that has little basic coaching in what is involved to run a supply firm. At the same time, we could ask how much first-hand knowledge do the suppliers have of the day-to-day management of a dental practice?

The increasing use of information technology

Modern technology has now moved us to the point where a practice's entire ordering system can be placed through a computer modem, with built-in cost check, previous order history, shopping lists, and so on. This is a valuable service, just as is the improved speed with which the order reaches the practice.

However, this is only one part of the service relationship—the order, the delivery, and the payment end. And there is a real danger of the technology itself eclipsing the other part—the offer, the new knowledge (the features, advantages and benefits to the practice of the product), and even the wisdom behind the decision to purchase. Instead of freeing the purchaser for a wider range of products, thus making a wider range of procedures available to patients, the unwary can become tied to the process of ordering and buying.

It may be that there is a choice, but the choice boils down to a decision about the cost of similar products from similar suppliers. The opportunity for the practice to develop and become increasingly sophisticated in its attitude to the dental supply market is stifled by the need to maintain a standard, routine, 'safe', electronic purchasing system.

In effect, the relationship between dental practice and dental supplier can become diminished by the buying process, just as the relationship between the practice and the patient can be confined by the system which governs the payment for dental care. The concept of a team working together is lost in the need to serve an increasingly tighter 'bottom-line'.

Developing the relationship

So, while bravely embracing the new technology (and it is vital we do so), both the quality practice and the quality supply company, must take every opportunity to raise their performance and create an extra layer of contact between them. This may need to involve modern electronic communication networks, but it requires one underlying principle to make it work—the building and maintaining of a personal relationship between those who use the product and those who supply it.

Therefore, if the practice team is consistently building a level of 'mutual respect' in terms of relationships with patients and colleagues (Chapter 2), it will also wish to do so with everyone else who has dealings with the practice. The first objective is to build the relationship—at whatever level is appropriate to the service being offered, and the onus is not just on the supplier. The practice team, every member of it, also has a responsibility to build and maintain a close relationship with its suppliers. After all, the outcome of every procedure within the practice is governed by the standard of equipment and materials purchased for the purpose—every bit as much as the training and experience of those using them.

Expectations

In a large practice, it may be that one person is responsible for purchasing. In a small practice, the system may involve everyone. But whatever the system, the first duty is to establish a connection between the expectations of the practice and the expectations of the supplier. These expectations may place an emphasis on the quality of materials, the ease of ordering, speed of delivery, cost or payment time: it may be all, some or none of these. At the same time the need of the practice to learn about new equipment and materials requires a steady flow of information, just as it does with technicians, not just in the form of brochures, but some means of viewing products and trying them out—hands-on experience. A large exhibition, like Dental Showcase, is one way of achieving the latter. Attendance at a course is another.

In-practice training

Visits by representatives of the supplying firm to the practice are also useful, but their usefulness is diminished unless a member of the team is free to see them when they arrive. The reality of visiting several dental practices in one day often means that it is impossible to predict a precise appointment time. Dental practices are busy places and tend, quite rightly, to favour the patient over any other interruption, so the enthusiastic representative ends up waiting and can go away disappointed.

Far better to find a way of making an appointment at a mutually convenient time and having a specific agenda—'something old, something new . . . !' A review of earlier purchases and a short demonstration of a new product, even a short session showing a new team-member how to mix or maintain one of the items regularly used in the practice, must surely create a greater feeling of mutual appreciation, and the basis for a more successful business relationship.

Of course, this would mean visiting less practices in an area over a given time, but there is no reason why it should not occur over certain periods of the year, reverting to the 'traditional' way at other times. The onus is on supplier and practice to decide on their mutual expectations and live up to them.

Shared courses

Yet another way to work together might be to share training between the practice team and the supplier's team. Striking a balance between expertise, service and management is as much a challenge for one as it is for the other. It is not so much a question of turning a profession into a business as of increasing the understanding of what constitutes business responsibilities, what constitutes professional responsibilities and where the balance lies. Shared training creates opportunities in areas that computer ordering can never approach.

It may not be realistic to expect every interaction between supplier and practice to work at this close a level, but it is surely realistic to work towards it. If used with a degree of wisdom, the tension between what actually happens in the relationship and what is expected to happen creates an energy that can make it an effective exercise for both parties.

Specialists

The point has already been made about the importance of the specialist to the team (Chapter 4). Exactly the same attitude applies to specialists as to everyone else outside the practice—the relationship is one to be developed, it is not there by right.

In the past, consultants consulted from the depth of a hospital, and the relationship was hampered by the organisational needs of the institution and the hierarchical expectations of custom. This is generally less so today. Attitudes have changed with the demands of the marketplace and specialist departments are becoming more accessible.

At the same time, there is an increasing emphasis on specialist practices, and this, no doubt, will grow. Such practices function facing the same challenges as every dental practice in building a practice team. The difference comes in the need for the specialist practitioner to build close ties with general practitioners, and this comes through shared courses, reciprocal visits to practices and a two-way flow of information. The 'Expectations' statement is relevant here also.

Colleagues outside the practice

There is a fourth group that also come under the heading of team-members. They include dentists and team-members from other practices or those who have no direct connection with the dental profession, but who have complementary knowledge, attitudes and skills. In order to understand the importance of building working relationships with these people, it is useful to review the concept of the 'master-mind alliance'.

The Master-Mind Group

Early this century, Napoleon Hill put forward seventeen principles for success in business. In one of these, which he named the master-mind principle, he suggested that permanent success cannot be achieved by one person alone, he needs to work with other people in what Hill called a 'master-mind alliance'. He was very specific about the principles that underlined such an alliance (Figure 5.2).

Although the language is different, we have already looked at these principles. This is team-building for a specific purpose—in your case, the success of your practice. Napoleon Hill put together a series of teams, from outside his immediate business situation, to achieve outcomes that would not have been possible otherwise.

He gathered information that was already available to anyone who took the trouble to study it. He went out of his way to meet people who were successful in their field. He studied their *experience*—both what happened to them, and what they *did* with what happened to them. He then put the results of his study to good use, not just for himself but for the benefit of his contemporaries and those who came after him. This, surely, is what is meant by a 'professional' approach. ('Professionalism is that quality

1. Adopt a **definite purpose** with an objective to be attained by the alliance;
2. Determine what **appropriate benefit each member** may receive in return for his/her cooperation in the alliance, and **see that he/she gets it**;
3. Establish a plan through which **each member makes a definite contribution**;
4. **Ensure that harmony prevails** in the group, (this requires a combination of communication and relationship-building skills);
5. Remember that your watchword is **definiteness of plan and purpose**;
6. Calculate the **number of individuals** in the group by the **nature of the purpose** to be attained.

Fig. 5.2 The Master-Mind Alliance
'The coordination of effort between two or more people in a spirit of perfect harmony in order to attain a specific objective'

Napoleon Hill

of conduct which accompanies the use of superior knowledge, care, skill and judgement, towards the benefit of another person or a society, prior to a consideration of self interest.' Dr L.D. Pankey)

The Information Overload

As with other professions, and in other walks of life, ideas that were considered radical twenty years ago have become readily acceptable now. Issues that seemed to hang on half-understood and barely tenable information have now been absorbed into the general psyche of the profession as 'new' information has become readily available. Often it is not so much new information, but old information presented in a way that the more pragmatic among us can more readily accept.

As an aside, it is perhaps helpful to recognise that just because a product or an idea is new and comes with a 'golden halo' of applause, it doesn't make it instantly acceptable. The computer industry found this out very early on. They were concerned that their prediction that there would be a personal computer in every home within ten years failed to materialise. Some useful research uncovered a way of categorising computer customers that can equally apply in other areas (Figure 5.3).

The Experimenters—like to try new things out—the hi-tec industry is perfect for these people
The Early Adopters—will take it on the moment they can see a good use for it
The Pragmatists—will take it on once it is obvious it is here to stay
The Late Adopters—have to be heavily encouraged to take it on
The Resisters—will not take it on under any circumstances

Fig 5.3 Just because something is 'new' it doesn't mean everyone will automatically embrace it

Nowadays information itself has become the focus of our attention, and awareness of issues, whether radical or not, is a direct result not just of how the information is presented, but who has the key to it. In the late 1990s, the difficulty is not so much in finding potentially useful information (and I include skills in this), but in sifting it out. For the dental practitioner and his team, getting hold of the right sort of information at the right time, turning it into knowledge and skills, and then applying it effectively in our practices—this is a major challenge.

The Mentor System

One way in which this can be managed is the increasingly attractive mentor system. A mentor can be compared to a coach—where the 'student' lacks skills, a coach would be appropriate, where he has the skills but is inexperienced in the job, then a mentoring relationship is more appropriate. The mentor gets to know the 'student', and acts as a guide while he finds his feet. Depending on the situation, the mentor uses his experience to help the student recognise the choices open to him and so further his career.

In a formal arrangement, an organisation might set up a network of mentors. The student, whether undergraduate, postgraduate or engaged in continued learning, is given a choice of mentors who live as locally as possible. The student and mentor then decide on the details of the relationship—how often they meet, expectations and so on. The organisation might follow up the relationship to see how it is developing. Alternatively, the 'student' might set out to find his own mentors.

The value of such a system is that, as the student, you set the pace and make the decisions. If you are going to take control of your practice and make it a permanent success, you have to set the agenda and supply the energy, but, as Napoleon Hill pointed out, you can't do it alone—you need someone to work with you, if only for a short while. A 'parent' organisation might take the initiative and give you a start by recommending someone to work with. But how you build on this is entirely up to you.

Gateways to knowledge

I have mentioned the 'information overload' and the fact that, to build our individual practices, we need access to the right type of information—at the right time. Not only do individual dental practice teams each operate their own practice models, but these models are continually evolving, giving a strong creative element to what we do. Therefore, there is a need for a reliable source of trustworthy, high-value information—on demand.

So there is a need for dental organisations of all descriptions to become gateways, (note: not gatekeepers) to the knowledge, skills and attitudes of their members; to act as resources, enabling members to work through the webs of information that face them daily, and allowing them to set up whatever systems are currently appropriate. In computer jargon, this is known as 'infomapping'!

Building a personal network

Information based on direct experience is particularly valuable when the person supplying that experience is well-known to the recipient (Chapter 2—mutual acceptance). The stronger the *personal* network, the more experience is made available to the practice and the more your experience is available to others. The challenge is to creatively use the various media open to us, initially in the form of courses and mentors, study clubs and conferences, and furthered by the use of telephone, mail, fax, e-mail, the Internet and so on.

A learning network

The art of learning is not just about your ability to absorb information, but also your ability to change appropriately with it. This can be very invigorating, but at times it can be a painful and confusing process. By widening the focus of your team, deliberately making yourselves accessible and your systems flexible, you will develop an active resource not just for you and your patients, but for other teams across the country. The experience of each team is not merely shared but built upon, and the resultant 'learning network' thus becomes a place of dynamic growth. The overall effect will be to ease the process of change, and to gain a wider and deeper understanding of a profession which, like every other profession, is making its way through an increasingly complex world.

6

and it is modified by every single patient . . .

The practice–patient relationship

With the exception of clinical emergencies, dental treatment has been correctly described as an optional procedure within a voluntary relationship. The patient has a choice. If they are going to make that choice, whether now or in the future, then our relationship with them is all-important.

In putting together our practice team, we have been looking at the very skills and attitudes required to build that relationship between the dentist, each member of the team and the patient. I have suggested that these skills and attitudes of working together become part of the culture of the practice.

The Golden Rule of dental care is 'care for each and every patient as you would wish them to care for you if they had your skills'.

For most of us that would mean with understanding and empathy. We would like care based on our personal situation, not modified by whatever is going on within the practice. We don't expect the team to be all-knowing or all-skilful, but we do expect them to use the full weight of their knowledge and skills and, where it is absent, and if appropriate, we expect to be referred to someone who does have the knowledge and skill to help us.

Thus, we, as patients, are expecting the practice team to create the conditions where care is patient-based, not practice-based. If the team is working at its optimum effectiveness, these conditions should be not only possible for every patient, but inevitable.

Barriers to a caring professional relationship

So, what can get in the way of our achieving this? Is it the pattern of the day—the way we schedule our workload? Perhaps it's the distraction of our own personal problems? Perhaps it's money, or time or effort. A psychotherapist, Gaie Houston, put it this way, 'I feel in my bones, as you probably do, that if I start off feeling defensive, grim, narrow-eyed, I have probably reduced to zilch my chance of helping that person.'

If we are going to provide the standard of care that is expected of us, we must raise our performance above the humdrum of our daily existence and reach out to the other person. At times, most times I hope, this is very easy. We project a confident reflection of our own self-esteem, a confidence in our ability. At other times, it is not so easy. We have to work very hard to shake off distraction and to concentrate wholly on the person seeking our care.

A classic example of this is the mental step required to 'let go' of the last patient and 'gear up' for the next. Dentistry is a very demanding occupation, and requires deep concentration. But the concentration required for one patient is different from the concentration required for the next. It is important to be able to clear our minds for the next person if we are going to treat each one as an individual. This means allowing time between patients to do this.

In Chapter 4, we looked at the factors that motivate and those that demotivate in the relationship between team-members—the same factors will cause patients to become motivated or demotivated.

Expectations

One of our early actions in planning our team was to write down our expectations. As patients, we have expectations also. Newsome (see References in Appendix) described the seven Cs used by patients to evaluate a dental practice (Figure 6.1):

Cues	Did I like the physical surroundings?
Comfort	Was the treatment painful?
Convenience	Could I organise my visits for a time that was convenient for me?
Care	Was the work done properly?
Communication	Was everything explained to me?
Courtesy	Was I treated fairly and with respect?
Cost	Did I get value for money?

Fig. 6.1 The seven Cs used by patients to evaluate a dental practice

As patients, most of us would like reassurance on these areas, and we would feel actively supported by the team if this were to happen. It would make us feel more comfortable—more accepted. Therefore, when a new patient comes into the practice, one of the tasks is to make sure these concerns are addressed in some way.

How it is done will depend on the practice and the team. In some practices, different members of the team deal with different areas of concern. This works where the team is mature and performing well, but there is a danger of only part of the message getting through. Another approach would be to pair a team-member with the patient. That team-member would then become responsible for the patient's dental care and liaise with the dentist on progress.

In addressing expectations, we are crossing one of the barriers to our professional relationship. We are increasing rapport, and with an increase in rapport comes the prospect of choice.

Choice—a matter of ethics

Building a professional relationship with our patients places a responsibility on our shoulders for the way we approach their care. We have the skills and knowledge to deal with their problems, but what about our attitude regarding their choice in whether they accept our advice?

There is always a choice in what we do, and all choices have consequences. From the team's point of view, we have to be aware that our patients do have a choice (they don't have to do what we say), and we have to be very clear about how they are making that choice, and whether they respect their decision. The ethical questions the team has to ask itself are 'What are we doing?' 'What for?' and 'Why?' The quality of these questions is lifted by the quality of the communication. Sondell and Soderfeldt suggested there were three purposes of dentist–patient communication:

- to create a good interpersonal relationship;
- to exchange information;
- to make treatment-related decisions.

Informed consent

Throughout this book we have been looking at building a series of relationships in such a way that the team-members will understand, from personal experience, what is required of an interpersonal relationship with their patients. One of the suggestion we made was to use employment legislation as a baseline for our team-building—'we have to comply with the legislation, but, in fact, we are setting out to have higher standards than that'.

By the same token, the concept of informed consent gives us a baseline for the information that we pass on to our patients. Graham *et al.* have pointed out that in the future, the principle of informed consent will likely apply to:

1. The dental treatment plan options available to the patient
2. Patient–dentist communication, including the obligation of the dentist to initiate discussion and/or answer any questions the patient has about:
   - the risks attached to the particular dental practice (e.g. water line contamination)
   - the infection control system used in the practice
   - the dental materials used, including amalgam and fluoride etc.
   - possible referral options—why and to whom
   - the final prognosis, i.e. the likelihood that the proposed treatment will succeed or fail, and the likely consequences.

We have already dealt with some of these in 'expectations'. Once again one of the main tasks of our team is to make sure that this happens, and the different approaches open to us were described in Chapter 2.

This brings us to the final factor in team-building. If we assign a certain member of the team to a particular patient, can we tell whether they will get on? Or must we guess? Given that we care for a wide variety of people from all walks of life, just how do we teach new members of our team to develop effective working relationships with our patients and treat them as individuals.

Social Style/Management Style

In their book, *Social Style/Management Style*, Robert and Dorothy Bolton make the point that all of us have a distinct style that applies to most of our actions. The crucial dimensions are 'assertiveness' and 'responsiveness'. The degree to which a person is perceived as assertive or responsive determines that person's social style. (An outline will be sufficient here. For a full account, I highly recommend this book.)

Assertiveness can be described as the degree to which a person's behaviour can be seen as forceful or directive. **Responsiveness** is defined as the degree by which a person's behaviour is seen by others as being emotionally expressive or emotionally controlled.

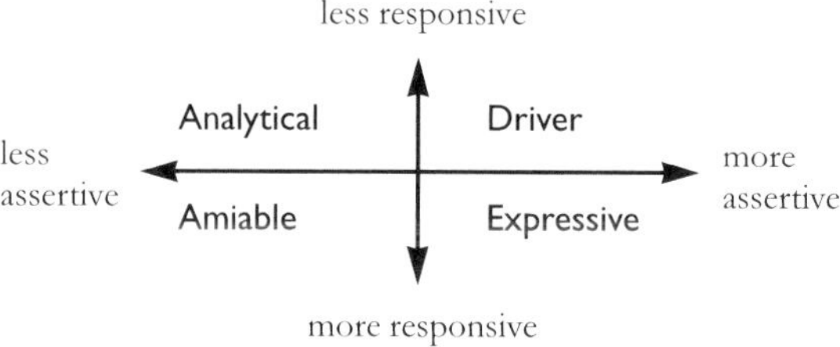

Fig. 6.2 The Social Style Grid

Figure 6.2 contains a grid, the horizontal axis being the degree of assertiveness, and the vertical axis the degree of responsiveness. These give four quadrants, which represent the four social styles—Analytical, Amiable, Driver and Expressive. **Analytical** is in the top left quadrant. People showing this style tend to be less assertive and show less emotion. They tend to be precise, deliberate and systematic in their approach to their work—many dentists fall into this category, (but certainly not all dentists). **Amiables**, on the other hand, also show less assertiveness but have a more emotional response. They tend to be sympathetic to the needs of others and sensitive to what lies under another person's behaviour. A person who is Amiable will make a very caring assistant.

The **Expressives**, being more emotional and also more assertive, tend to be flamboyant people. They like fun, and humour, and can lift those around them. They are very 'up front' and represent the practice well to the outside world. Finally, the **Driver** shows a high level of assertiveness with a high level of emotional control. He gets to the point quickly and expresses himself succinctly. He is decisive, results-oriented, objective and pragmatic. He like to get things done. A Driver in the dental chair is not going to allow a great deal of small talk. He will want to know what, why, when and how, the benefits of treatment, and will then make a decision. The Amiable on the other hand will be happy to talk about other things, and not worry too much about time passing.

I made the point earlier about labels (p. 28), and it still applies. These are for planning purposes; we are making decisions about how best to relate to people. The Social Style model is useful because it is based on the other person's behaviour and how it relates to our own. A person may show a cluster of behaviours that would indicate how expressive or responsive she is. For example, a well-known entertainer like Shirley Bassey might be considered an Expressive, whereas a prominent businessman like Rupert Murdoch might be a Driver, and so on.

As I have mentioned, the value of the model comes in understanding the effect one style has on another. For example, Analyticals and Drivers have their relative lack of responsiveness in common and might complement each other in a business situation (accountant and manager?). On the other hand, an Amiable, with his high responsiveness and low assertiveness, has little in common with a Driver. Their styles are diametrically opposed, and are less likely to get on. You might think twice about leaving your caring assistant to look after the high-powered businessman who is in a hurry—let your Analytical receptionist sort out the details. Similarly, you, the Analytical dentist, may sometimes find the Expressive patient trying—'Why does that patient have to keep sitting up and talking?'

Care for the individual

With a working understanding of Social Style, relating to patients as individuals becomes a more practical prospect in a busy practice. It is easy for team-members to understand and use, and, in effect, it creates a level-playing field for the team—they can all relate to it equally. This brings us back to Bud Ham—'When people meet in face-to-face interaction, they will come to respect one another if they meet in a state of equality.'

A lifetime's study

This is the end of our introduction to team-building and the beginning of your work on it. If you have read this through quickly, I hope you have marked those areas that you might look at again. If you have already been through it once, then I hope you will recognise this one critical point—working with other people is not the subject of a short study period, and then 'you've either got it or you haven't'. It is a lifetime's study. Every new person you meet is different from the last one, and every person you already know is growing in some subtle way—and so are you. As the title of the book says, a dental practice team is a very special team. I hope it continues to be special for you.

Postscript

. . . and it has wider implications too

In the past, a special relationship between the dentist and the patient has been at the heart of a successful dental practice. The primary objective of this book has been to encourage the reader to think of team-building, not as some separate activity, but as the central focus of the practice, and to recognise the value of the *practice*–patient relationship. This doesn't deny the importance of the dentist–patient relationship, but, in widening the scope of the relationship, it acknowledges the expectations of an increasingly aware population.

However, in encouraging the concept of relationship-building, we must also acknowledge that man has been a social being for thousands of years, and has faced the challenges of working together and relationship-building through all that time. There have been times when he has achieved this with awe-inspiring success, and there have been other times when he has failed spectacularly. And, as we look around the world today, we see that failure still happens, even after thousands of years of trying. It obviously isn't that easy! Surely we have all experienced the challenges involved.

Therefore, to make out a case for relationships, knowing that success is not guaranteed, may seem over-confident, even arrogant, however unintentional. So, at this late stage, it may be helpful to make a distinction between arrogance and confidence. Arrogance says, 'I know what I know, it is correct, this is how things are and I will look no further, whatever your views.' Confidence, on the other hand, says, 'I know what I know, this is how things appear to be. I appreciate you have your own views and are probably looking at the same thing from a different direction. I am happy to make my case and listen to yours. If you can come up with a better solution, then so be it, I will review my ideas and move on. In the meantime, you are welcome to lean on my ideas while you consider whether they may be helpful to you.'

We are currently moving into a new millennium, a mere pin-prick in the thousands of years man has existed. We are faced with a pace of change unimagined even thirty years ago, and methods of communication that rely on an evolving technology that most of us have difficulty keeping up with, let alone using effectively. And yet there is one type of communication that will not change—face-to-face, one-to-one, you and me. As we try to embrace this new technology (and we really must do so), we mustn't forget those older skills, the ones that lifted dentistry from craft to profession. If those of us who make use of them daily start to neglect them, what chance has everyone else?

I am confident that to create a relationship-based dental practice is to create a successful dental practice and I commend it to you.

Appendix

References

Graham, P.E., Harel-Raviv, M. 'The future of informed consent and patient–dentist communication' *Journal of the Canadian Dental Association* 1997 Jun **63**(6): 460–3

Heron, J. *Six Category Intervention Analysis*, 1st edn, p.2, Guildford: Human Potential Research Project, Department of Educational Studies, University of Surrey, 1975

Herzberg, Frederick *Motivation to Work* 12th edn, New York: Transaction Publishers, 1993

Levin, R.P. 'Creating a team of practice builders' *JCO* 1993 Aug **27**(8): 437–41

Maslow, A. *Motivation and Personality* 3rd edn, New York: Harper and Row, 1987

Newsome, P. 'Consumer satisfaction and the success of your practice, Part 1, Why is consumer satisfaction so important?' *Dental Business* 1997 **2**(4): 10–13

Sondell, K. Soderfelt B. 'Dentist-patient communication: a review of relevant models.' [Review] [119 refs] *Acta Odontalgia Scandinavia* 1997 Apr **55**(2): 116–26

Further reading

Chapter 2: Your team begins with you . . .

Rogers, Carl, *On Becoming a Person*, (19th Reprint), London: Constable, 1996

Covey, Stephen, *The 7 Habits of Highly Effective People*, New York: Fireside (Simon & Schuster), 1989

Gerber, Michael, *The E-myth Revisited*, New York: HarperBusiness, 1995

Chapter 3: it builds on one-to-one relationships . . .

Bennis, Warren, *On Becoming a Leader*, London: Century Business, 1989

Ham, O.A. Bud, *You Are in The Right Place*, Aurora: The White Feather Press, 1995

McGinnis, Alan Loy, *Bringing Out the Best in People*, Minneapolis: Augsburg, 1985

Chapter 4: it develops into a small group of dedicated professionals . . .

Landsberg, Max, *The TAO of Coaching*, London: HarperCollins, 1996

Jameson, Cathy, *Great Communication=Great Production*, Tulsa: Pennwell Books, 1994

Ham, O.A. Bud, *The Best of the Best—a collection of articles on practice management from 1982–85*, Aurora: The White Feather Press, 1985

Bonnington, Christopher, *The Everest Years*, London: Hodder & Stoughton, 1986

Chapter 6: and it is modified by every single patient

Bolton, Robert and Dorothy, *Social Style/Management Style*, New York: American Management Associations, 1984

Postscript: . . . and it has wider implications too

de Bono, Edward, *Textbook of Wisdom*, London: Penguin Books, 1997

Tapes

Chapter 5: it reaches well beyond your practice walls . . .

Hill, Napoleon, *The Science of Personal Achievement*, Illinois: Nightingale-Conant Corporation, (in the UK—Long Road, Paignton, Devon TQ4 7BB)

Diary systems

DayTimer Diary System, (inc. software). Day-Timers Europe Ltd, John Tate Road, Foxholes Business Park, Hertford, Herts, SG13 7DT.

Psion 3a / 3c /5 palmtop computers. Psion plc, Alexander House, 85 Frampton Street, London NW8 8NQ

Afterword

'A Very Special Team' is an *introduction* to team-building, and this is reflected in the short list in the Appendix. The books and articles are the ones I turned to for immediate reference. They cover a wide spectrum: from the practical—Cathy Jameson's down-to-earth advice on communication within the dental practice and Max Landsberg on coaching—to the more thought-provoking—Bud Ham's insight into building trust (Chapter 3, p. 35). In between, Stephen Covey's 'principle-centred' approach presents a powerful basis for success, and Chris Bonnington's account of his expeditions demonstrates the challenges faced by strong individuals working in tight conditions where teamwork is vital. These volumes are a tiny example of a very wide and rich bibliography on the subject, which I hope you will discover and explore for yourself.

You may ask, 'Why should I take time out to read about team-building, when, of all the things I have done since the day I was born, being with other people is the one I am most familiar with? I should be out doing, not sitting reading!' Well, of course, working with others is *the* activity for us all. We all do it all the time. However, familiarity does not necessarily lead to skill, and team-building is a skill in which, paradoxically, success is partly due to the recognition of how much more there is to know.

The aspiring team-leader enters a learning cycle which starts with an attitude—an acceptance of the potential depth and breadth of the human relationship and a willingness to learn more. He/she moves on to a search for more knowledge (some of which is found in books!), and enters a practical phase—turning that knowledge into experience. From this experience, new skills arise, which lead to a revision of attitudes, demanding, in their turn, new knowledge, further experience, more skills and so on—a continuously widening spiral that is with the now-successful leader forever.

Learning, therefore, is an essential ingredient of the team leader's work-in-progress. It doesn't matter whether he/she is overloaded with skills or experience or knowledge or attitudes. It is moving from one to another that leads to fruitful change. Team-building is an alive, vital, daily activity, and requires alive, vital, aware people to achieve success. If you are serious in your search for progress in your practice, then take what you have learned here, explore other people's ideas, marry them to your own experience, and use the blend to lift yourselves and those around you to greater achievement. The result will be a happy, fulfilling and effective practice.

Index